THE ACADEMIC EDGE LTD.

Physics Grade 11

Go Beyond Your Limits

ISBN: 1-55202-027-4

The Academic Edge Ltd.

Congratulations! You are obviously very interested in investing in yourself and becoming the best you can be. Our curriculum-based guides are supplemental learning aids that provide uncomplicated and straightforward explanations, examples, exercises, solutions and practice tests.

The study guides are intended to assist you, the student, in understanding key concepts and in developing the necessary skills that will enable you to achieve maximum results in school or government exams. Combined with classroom instruction, reading and practice received from your school resources, these guides will be an invaluable asset in achieving your academic goals.

The Academic Edge Ltd. commissioned experts in their specific areas to develop our study guides. The mandate is to provide useful guides that are curriculum specific to offer you an alternative resource – a study companion that will enhance your efforts. **"A personal tutor in a book".**

Challenge yourself to "GO BEYOND YOUR LIMITS"

The Academic Edge Ltd.

The Academic Edge Ltd.
1-800-403-4751
aestudyguides.com

Something about the Author:

I'm Christine Lesiak. I got my B.Sc. in physics from the University of New Brunswick in 1993. It was working as a teaching assistant in undergraduate physics labs over the last few years, at both the University of New Brunswick and the University of Alberta, that I discovered a love of teaching.

I had a great time writing this study guide for you, and hope you find it helpful in your course work. I would like to leave you with a bit of advice I always give my students; If you don't understand, *ask*! That's why your teacher is there. There's no such thing as a stupid question.

One other thing before I let you get on with it. I need to thank Lori Reid, for her help proofreading, and *huge* thanks my husband, Marc MacKenzie, who did most of the figures in the last part of this study guide.

If this is the vision of the future; if this is the direction in which we want to move. Well then, we next have to decide what we are going to do to get it done. Visions are not self fulfilling. We cannot stand idly by and expect dreams to come true on their own power.

The future is not a gift it is an achievement.

Robert F. Kennedy, 1968

PHYSICS GRADE 11

Table of Contents

PHYSICS GRADE 11

PHYSICS GRADE 11

PHYSICS GRADE 11

PHYSICS GRADE 11

The ABC's of Physics

One of the hardest parts of learning about physics is learning the language. It's not a language in the way we're used to thinking about them. It's more like the languge of street signs, where we communicate ideas with symbols. When we learned to read, we had to learn our letters (which are also symbols) before we could read sentences. The same thing is true for physics. We have to know what all the mathematical symbols are, and what they mean, before we can understand how to put them together in a way that makes sense.

Most of the symbols that physicists use are mathematical ones, so you already have the basic grammar down with adding, subtracting, multiplying and dividing.

Scientific Notation

Sometimes we have to use very large or very small numbers. When we do, it's a big pain to write out all those zeros all the time. A billion is nine zeros (1 000 000 000), so it's much easier to use a shorthand called scientific notation rather than write those zeros all the time. A billion in scientific notation is written 10^9 or 1×10^9 (multiplying by 1 doesn't change the value of the number) because $10 \times 10 \times 10 \times 10 \times 10 \times 10 \times 10 \times 10 \times 10 = 10^9 = 1$ billion. A positive exponent means that the decimal place has been moved to the left to write a large number in scientific notation. A negative exponent means that the decimal place has been moved to the right to write a small number in scientific notation.

> **Example:** $2\ 540\ 000 = 2.54 \times 10^6$ is a large number, so has a positive exponent. The decimal place was moved six places to the left.
>
> $0.000\ 872\ 4 = 8.724 \times 10^{-4}$ is a small number, so has a negative exponent. The decimal place was moved four places to the right.

These are some general rules for exponents;

Exponent multiplication rule: Add the exponents.

$$10^a \times 10^b = 10^{a+b} \quad \text{or} \quad 10^a \times 10^{-b} = 10^{a-b}$$

> **Examples:**
>
> $$10^{12} \times 10^3 = 10^{12+3} = 10^{15}$$
>
> $$10^{-12} \times 10^3 = 10^{(-12)+3} = 10^{-9}$$

Exponent division rule: Subtract the exponent in the denominator (the number under the division line) from the exponent in the numerator (the number over the division line).

$$\frac{10^0}{10^a} = \frac{1}{10^a} = 10^{-a} \quad \textbf{or} \quad \frac{10^a}{10^b} = 10^{a-b}$$

> **Examples:**
>
> $$\frac{1}{10^{-5}} = 10^{-(-5)} = 10^5$$
>
> $$\frac{10^4}{10^3} = 10^{4-3} = 10^1 = 10$$
>
> $$\frac{10^{-24}}{10^{30}} = 10^{(-24)-30} = 10^{-54}$$

PHYSICS GRADE 11

Units

In physics, we try to describe and predict what we see in the world around us. How fast did that bike go ? If I dropped this water ballon on Chris' head, how long would I have to run away before he got soaked ? To do this, we have to take measurements, using standard units. Some of the units we use all the time are meters, inches, seconds, kilograms, pounds and years. The one thing all units have in common is that there's some kind of definition of exactly how big (heavy, long) it is. Scientists throughout the world use the SI system (Système Internationale d'Unités). Some of the base units (units which are used to define other derived units) in the SI system are;

Some Base SI Units

<u>quantity</u>	<u>unit</u>	<u>symbol</u>
length	meter	m
mass	kilogram	kg
time	second	s

We'll define derived units as we need them.

We're all used to saying 'a kilometer' instead of '1000 meters', or '10^3 meters', as a shortcut. There are thirteen standard prefixes we use as shortcuts to express multiplying by factors of ten in scientific notation.

PHYSICS GRADE 11

Standard Prefixes for Multiples of Ten

Prefix	Symbol	Factor
tera	T	10^{12}
giga	G	10^{9}
mega	M	10^{6}
kilo	k	10^{3}
hecto	h	10^{2}
deka	da	10^{1}
deci	d	10^{-1}
centi	c	10^{-2}
milli	m	10^{-3}
micro*	μ	10^{-6}
nano	n	10^{-9}
pico	p	10^{-12}
femto	f	10^{-15}

*μ is a Greek letter, pronounced 'miu'.

What this table tells you, is that there are 10^{9} seconds in a gigasecond, 10^{3} meters in a kilometer, or 10^{-6} grams in a microgram. Now you can see why scientific notation will come in handy.

What is 5 grams + 3 meters ? Adding these two number together makes no sense, because they are different types of quantities, one is a mass and the other is a length. We can't add (or subtract) numbers which are different types of quantities, but we can add together two numbers of the same type, but different units.

Example:

$$5.000 \text{ m} + 4 \text{ mm} = 5.000 \text{ m} + 4 \times 10^{-3} \text{ m}$$
$$= 5.000 \text{ m} + 0.004 \text{ m}$$
$$= 5.004 \text{ m}$$

These are two important things to remember.

1- We can't add together numbers that describe different physical quantities. i.e. you can't add mass and time.

2- We have to be careful to make sure units that are different, but describe the same physical quantity are expressed in the SAME units before adding (or subtracting).

Example: *What if you want to add 5 g and 3.00 hg ?*

We'll convert the grams into hectograms first.

$$5\text{g} = \frac{5\text{g}}{\frac{10^2\,\text{g}}{1\text{hg}}} = 5\text{g} \times \frac{1\text{hg}}{10^2\,\text{g}} = 5\text{g} \times 10^{-2}\,\frac{\text{hg}}{\text{g}} = 5 \times 10^{-2}\,\text{hg} = 0.05\text{hg}$$

We can see that the grams cancel out algebraicly. This is how we can tell if we've done a conversion correctly; if the units we don't want all cancel each other out, leaving us only we the units we do want. Now we can add the masses,

$$0.05\text{ hg} + 3.00\text{ hg} = 3.05\text{ hg}$$

In this example, we had to convert to the same units in order to add the number. We did this by multiplying by a conversion factor. In this case, the conversion factor was 10^{-2} hg/g. It follows that we can multiply or divide by different units. In fact, we can even multiply or divide units that represent different type of quantities, and cancel out like you do in algebra. This is very important, and useful. It brings us to our next topic.

Unit Conversion

Example: *How many seconds are there in a day ?*

We know there are 24 hours in a day, 60 minutes in an hour, and 60 seconds in a minute, so

$$1\text{day} \times 24\frac{\text{hours}}{\text{day}} \times 60\frac{\text{min}}{\text{hour}} \times 60\frac{\text{s}}{\text{min}} = 1 \times 24 \times 60 \times 60\text{s}$$

$$= 216000\text{s}$$

There are 216 000 seconds in a day.

Example: *A car is travelling at 100 km/hour. How many meters/second (m/s) is this ?*

We know there are 10^3 m/km, 60 min/hour and 60 s/min. We'll convert the kilometers to meters first.

$$\frac{100\text{km}}{\text{hr}} \times 10^3\frac{\text{m}}{\text{km}} = 10^5\frac{\text{m}}{\text{hr}}$$

Now we'll convert the hours to seconds.

$$\frac{10^5\frac{\text{m}}{\text{hour}}}{60\frac{\text{min}}{\text{hour}} \times 60\frac{\text{s}}{\text{min}}} = 10^5\frac{\text{m}}{\text{hour}} \times \frac{1}{60}\frac{\text{hour}}{\text{min}} \times \frac{1}{60}\frac{\text{min}}{\text{s}} = \frac{10^5}{3600}\frac{\text{m}}{\text{s}}$$

$$= 27.8\frac{\text{m}}{\text{s}}$$

So the car is travelling at 27.8 m/s.

Units can be a big help when we're solving problems. We can use them to see if our answer makes sense. We already did this in the last few examples. Let's look at the last example again, the one with the car travelling at 100 km.hour.

$$\frac{10^5 \frac{m}{hour}}{60 \frac{min}{hour} \times 60 \frac{s}{min}} = 10^5 \frac{m}{hour} \times \frac{1}{60} \frac{hour}{min} \times \frac{1}{60} \frac{min}{s} = \frac{10^5}{3600} \frac{m}{s}$$

$$= 27.8 \frac{m}{s}$$

If I had made the mistake of *multiplying* 60 min/hour instead of dividing, I would have got the weird units $\frac{m \cdot min^2}{s}$. Since these units are not m/s, we know I screwed up somewhere. We're going to look at more dimensional analysis later.

Trigonometry

Some times we need to use some geometry to solve problems in science. If you can break a problem down into right angle triangles, the math we need is simple. A right angle triangle is a triangle with one angle equal to 90° (a right angle), like the triangle below. A box in a corner means that angle is 90°. The longest side of a right angle triangle is called the hypotenuse, and it is always opposite of the right angle. The other sides are called the opposite side, and the adjacent side as shown on the triangle below.

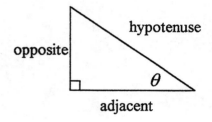

θ is the Greek letter 'theta'. It's usually used to represent an angle. In a right angle triangle, it's the angle between the adjacent side and the hypotenuse.

The trigonometric functions are sine, cosine and tangent, or sin, cos, and tan for short. They help us find angles by using a ratio of the side lengths. Sine, cosine, and tangent don't have any units, because they are a ratio. They are defined as;

$$\sin\theta = \frac{\text{length of opposite}}{\text{length of hypotenuse}} = \frac{\text{opp}}{\text{hyp}}$$

$$\cos\theta = \frac{\text{length of adjacent}}{\text{length of hypotenuse}} = \frac{\text{adj}}{\text{hyp}}$$

$$\tan\theta = \frac{\text{length of opposite}}{\text{length of adjacent}} = \frac{\text{opp}}{\text{adj}}$$

We can use these functions to find the lengths of sides of right-angle triangles.

Example: *What are the lengths of the unknown sides of the triangle below, if θ = 30° ?*

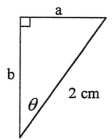

The hypotenuse is the side opposite the right angle, so its length is 2cm. The side opposite the angle θ is side a, and the side adjacent is side b.

Using the definitions for sine and cosine we defined above, we can find the missing lengths.

$$\sin\theta = \frac{\text{opp}}{\text{hyp}} = \frac{a}{2\text{cm}}$$

$$a = 2\text{cm} \cdot \sin\theta = 2\text{cm} \cdot \sin 30° = 1\text{cm}$$

The length of side a is 1 cm.

$$\cos\theta = \frac{\text{adj}}{\text{hyp}} = \frac{b}{2\text{cm}}$$

$$b = 2\text{cm} \cdot \cos\theta = 2\text{cm} \cdot \cos 30° = 1.73\text{cm}$$

The length of side b is 1.73cm.

Sometimes we know the length of the sides, and want to find the angles. In this case, we can use the inverse trigonometric functions. They are;

$$\theta = \sin^{-1}\left(\frac{opp}{hyp}\right)$$

$$\theta = \cos^{-1}\left(\frac{adj}{hyp}\right)$$

$$\theta = \tan^{-1}\left(\frac{opp}{adj}\right)$$

We have to be careful here, because the -1 exponent in these equations doesn't mean that we can take the reciprocal of the function. For the first equation, we can read it as 'θ equals the angle whose sine is the opposite side divided by the hypotenuse'.

Example: *Find θ and ϕ in the triangle below.*

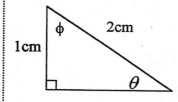

The hypotenuse is the side opposite of the right angle labeled 2cm. For angle the θ, we're given the opposite side = 1cm. For the angle ϕ, we know the adjacent side = 1cm.

So,
$$\theta = \sin^{-1}\left(\frac{opp}{hyp}\right) = \sin^{-1}\left(\frac{1cm}{2cm}\right) = 30°$$

and
$$\phi = \cos^{-1}\left(\frac{adj}{hyp}\right) = \cos^{-1}\left(\frac{adj}{hyp}\right) = 60°$$

Angle θ equals 30° , and angle ϕ equals 60°.

Another useful thing to know is the **Pythagorean theorem**. It says 'the square of the hypotenuse is equal to the sum of the squares of the other two sides'. Whoa...this is one of those things that's easier to understand in the language of math.

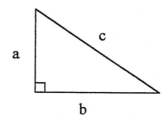

If we have a right triangle with side lengths of a, b, and c, the Pythagorean theorem says that: $a^2 + b^2 = c^2$. $a^2 + b^2 = c^2$

$$a^2 + b^2 = c^2 \qquad a^2 + b^2 = c^2$$

Example: *We know the length of the hypotenuse is 8cm, and the length of one of the sides is 5cm. What is the length of the other side ?*

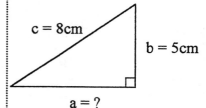

We can use the Pythagorean theorem, since we know two side lengths. We know that c = 8cm, and either a or b (it doesn't matter which one) is 5 cm. We'll choose b = 5cm.

So since $a^2 + b^2 = c^2$,

$$a^2 = c^2 - b^2$$

$$a = \sqrt{c^2 - b^2}$$

$$= \sqrt{8^2 \, cm^2 - 5^2 \, cm^2}$$

$$= \sqrt{64cm^2 - 25cm^2}$$

$$= \sqrt{39cm^2}$$

$$= 6.2cm$$

The length of the third side of the triangle is 6.2 cm.

All this trigonometry is *really* important for our next section, when we'll talk about vectors.

Vectors and Scalars

A **scalar** tells us how big something is; it tells us its **magnitude**. Take a bag of Gummi Bears. There are lots of scalars that describe it; the number of Gummi Bears in the bag, how much it weighs (which is important ! I usually have to pay by weight), the temperature of the bag... What a scalar *can't* tell us is where it is. It can't do this, because we need a direction. If you tell me that I can find the bag 5.3 meters (a scalar) from the chocolate rabbits, I'll get annoyed, because I'll have to look at each point that is 5.3 meters away from the chocolate rabbits, which is a circle of radius 5.3 meters (realistically, I'd stick with the *bunnies*... but that's not the point). However, if you tell me the bag is 5.3 meters *east* of the chocolate rabbits, I'll be able to find the Gummi Bears very quickly. This is because you've given me a **vector**, which tells me a magnitude *and* a direction.

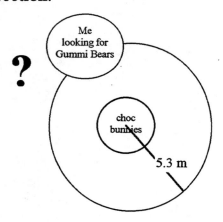

Looking for Gummi Bears
with no direction.

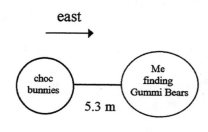

Easily finding Gummi Bears
given a direction.

A **magnitude** is a number which tells us how much there is.
A **scalar** has a magnitude. It is a quantity which can be described with a single number {temperature (T), mass (m), speed (s or v)}.
A **vector** has a magnitude and a direction. It is a quantity which needs to be described with at least two numbers. Some examples of vectors are velocity (v), acceleration (a), and position (x).

Let's look at a more traditional example. It's the difference between **speed** and **velocity**. Say we're traveling in my private jet (we all have our dreams), and the pilot tells us we're traveling at an average speed of 1000km/hour. That's very good, but we have no idea WHERE we're going. If she tells us we're traveling due east at a speed of 1000km/hour, we know where we're going, because she gave us a velocity.

How is this expressed in the language of math ? A scalar usually appears in italics. Mass is m, speed is s or v. A vector is shown in one of two ways. When we're writing them by hand, we usually put an arrow on top of the symbol. One of the symbols for the velocity vector is $\vec{v}$. In books (like this), vectors usually appear in bold type, like v (this is what I'll do). You may very well be wondering why a 'v' is used as a scalar v (speed), and as a vector v (velocity). Doesn't this get confusing ? Not really. Even though vectors contain the information for both size and direction, we don't always care what direction it's going, or it's pretty obvious. If I drop something from the CN tower, I'm pretty sure I know which way it's going to fall. We will often use the scalar notation for a vector when we're only interested about the magnitude.

Let's go back to my private jet;

Our velocity:	v = 1000 km/hour, due east.
Our speed (the magnitude of v):	v = 1000 km/hour

How To Use Vectors: Vector Diagrams and Addition

We often use **vector diagrams** (another element of the language) to help us picture what's going on in a problem. The vector diagram for our jet travel is this;

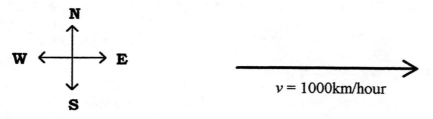

The arrow points in the direction of travel, and the length is proportional to the magnitude. If the magnitude were less, the arrow would be shorter. What if we have more that one vector ? This leads us to our next topic, vector addition.

Addition of parallel vectors

Say we're rollerblading down a straight, eastward path. We start at one end of the path (call it 'point A'), but stop 700m later to allow some goslings to cross the path at point B. We go for another 500m to point C before it starts to rain and have to catch a bus back home. We want to draw a vector diagram for our rollerblade excursion. We joint the vectors d_{AB} and d_{BC} so that the end of the second touches the head of the first.

The vector d_{AC} is the **resultant vector**, the vector we get when we add the other two. It always has its tail at the tail of the first vector, and its tip at the tip of the last.

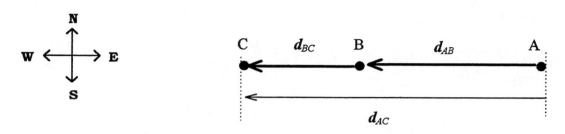

Written mathematically, it looks like this; $d_{AC} = d_{AB} + d_{BC}$

$$= 700 \text{ m east} + 500 \text{ m east}$$

$$= 1200 \text{ m east}$$

Now, say we turned around at point C, rather than waiting for the goslings. Then we would be going east between B and C, like this;

There's a trick here. We can only add 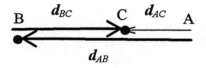 vectors that are going in the same direction. It's kind of like when we were adding quantities with units. The trick we use is to notice that going east is like going *negative* west.

We can say that $\quad d_{BC} \quad = 500\text{m east}$

$$= -500\text{m west}$$

So now; $\qquad d_{AC} \quad = d_{AB} + d_{BC}$

$$= 700\text{m west} - 500\text{m west}$$

$$= 200\text{m west}$$

We can add any number of parallel vectors the same way.

Addition of Perpendicular Vectors

Of course, when we go somewhere, we don't usually go in a straight line. We have to have some way of adding vectors together when we make turns. This time when we go out rollerblading we travel 500m north from point A, turn east at B, and go on for another 600m to C. The vector diagram for this is;

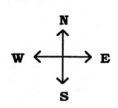

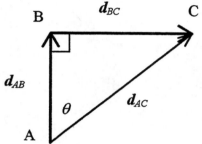

This is expressed mathematically as:

$$d_{AC} = d_{AB} + d_{BC}$$

$$= 500 \text{ m north} + 600 \text{ m east.}$$

Since the vectors aren't in the same direction, we can't add them like we did in the last section. This is where that trigonometry comes in handy. The triangle I drew is a right angle triangle, with the right angle at B, so we can use the Pythagorean theorem to find the length of the resultant vector (remember that the Pythagorean theorem is $a^2 + b^2 = c^2$, where c is the length of the hypotenuse, and a and b are the lengths of the other sides). So then the length of d_{AC} is;

$$(d_{AC})^2 = (d_{AB})^2 + (d_{BC})^2$$

$$d_{AC} = \sqrt{(d_{AB})^2 + (d_{BC})^2}$$

$$= \sqrt{(500)^2 + (600)^2} \text{ meters}$$

$$= \sqrt{250000 + 360000} \text{ meters}$$

$$= 781 \text{ meters}$$

Now, this is the magnitude of the vector. We need to use some more trigonometry to find the direction. We'll do this by finding the angle between the north vector (d_{AB}) and the resultant vector (d_{AC}). Since we know the lengths of all three sides, we could use any of sine, cosine, or tangent to find the angle. I'll use cosine this time.

$$\theta = \cos^{-1}\left(\frac{adj}{hyp}\right) = \cos^{-1}\left(\frac{d_{AB}}{d_{AC}}\right) = \cos^{-1}\left(\frac{500}{781}\right) = 50.2°$$

The direction is 50.2° east of north.

Now we know d_{AC} = 781 m, 50.2° east of north.

Vector Components

Up to now, we've talked about direction in relation to the compass directions. This isn't always the easiest way to do things. We often talk about direction relative to the x-y plane, like vector **A** below.

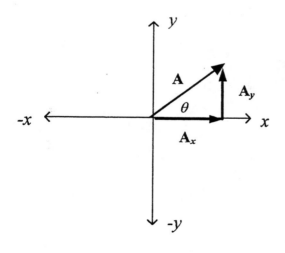

The vector's tail is at (0,0) in the x-y plane. The direction is given as an angle θ relative to the positive x-axis. Looking at this, we see that **A** has two **vector components, A_x** and **A_y**.

We can think of *any* vector as the sum of two **vector components**. One vector component is in the y-direction, and the other is in the x-direction. So, $A = A_x + A_y$

    To break a vector down into x and y vector components, we have to again call on our handy trigonometric tools.

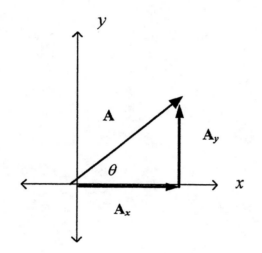

$$\sin \theta = \frac{opp}{hyp} = \frac{A_y}{A}$$

$$A_y = A \sin \theta$$

and

$$\cos \theta = \frac{adj}{hyp} = \frac{A_x}{A}$$

$$A_x = A \cos \theta$$

    Notice that we are again using magnitudes in our trigonometric calculations.

Example: *Find the vector components of the vector **p** if the magnitude p = 5 cm.*

We can use the sine and cosine trigonometric identities to find p_x and p_y..

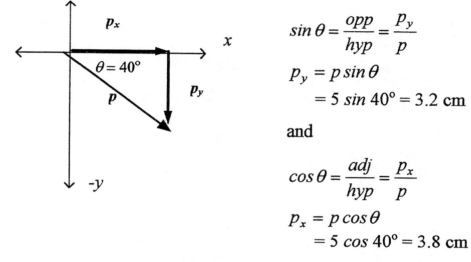

$$\sin \theta = \frac{opp}{hyp} = \frac{p_y}{p}$$

$$p_y = p \sin \theta$$
$$= 5 \sin 40° = 3.2 \text{ cm}$$

and

$$\cos \theta = \frac{adj}{hyp} = \frac{p_x}{p}$$

$$p_x = p \cos \theta$$
$$= 5 \cos 40° = 3.8 \text{ cm}$$

We have found $p_x = 3.2$ cm and $p_{xy} = 3.8$ cm, so then
$$p_x = 3.2 \text{ cm, positive x direction}$$
and $\qquad p_{xy} = 3.8$ cm, negative y direction.

Vector Component Addition

A really good question at this point is 'Why bother ?'. I'm sure you could have guessed that I wouldn't bother mentioning vector components if they we weren't going to use them for something. We can use vector components to add vectors that aren't either parallel or perpendicular. We do this by finding the vector components, then we can adding all the x-direction components together and all the y-direction components together. We can do this because all the x-direction (or y-direction) components *are in the same direction.*

Example: *Find the resultant vector* **q** = **r** + **t** *for the vector diagram below if r = 4 and t = 3.*

We can use the sine and cosine trigonometric identities to find the vector components of **r** and **t**.

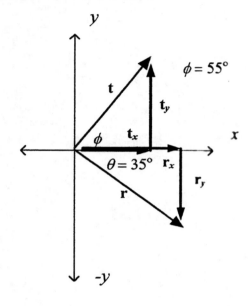

$$\sin \theta = \frac{opp}{hyp}$$

$$r_y = r \sin \theta = 4 \sin 35° = 2.3$$

$$t_y = t \sin \phi = 3 \sin 55° = 2.5$$

and

$$\cos \theta = \frac{adj}{hyp}$$

$$r_x = r \cos \theta = 4 \cos 35° = 3.3$$

$$t_x = t \cos \phi = 3 \cos 55° = 1.7$$

Now that we have the vector components of **t** and **r**, we add them to find the vector components of **q**. We are using vector notation (bold) for r_x, r_y t_x, and t_x now because we've also included a positive or negative direction for each component.

Vector	x component	y component
r	$r_x = +3.3$	$r_y = -2.3$
t	$t_x = +1.7$	$t_y = +2.5$

q	$q_x = r_x + t_x$	$q_y = r_y + t_y$
	$= +3.3 + (+1.7)$	$= (-2.3) + (+2.5)$
	$= +5.0$	$= +0.2$

Now we know that the vector **q** has components $q_x = +5.0$ and $q_y = +0.2$.

We can find the magnitude of **q** using the Pythagorean theorem;

$$q = \sqrt{(q_x)^2 + (q_y)^2}$$

$$= \sqrt{(5.0)^2 + (0.2)^2}$$

$$= \sqrt{25.04}$$

$$= 5.004 \text{ is the magnitude of } \mathbf{q}.$$

All that's left to do to find **q** is to find it's direction. We can easily find the angle (we'll call it angle α, the Greek letter alpha) between **q** and the positive x-axis now that we know the lengths of the sides of q_x and q_y by using the inverse tangent function.

$$\alpha = tan^{-1}\left(\frac{opp}{adj}\right) = tan^{-1}\left(\frac{q_y}{q_x}\right) = tan^{-1}\left(\frac{0.2}{5.0}\right)$$

$$= 2.3°$$

We now know that **q** = 5.004, 2.3° above the positive x-axis.

Let's draw vector **q**. We draw vectors **r** and **t** tip to tail, then draw **q** so that its tail is at the tail of **t**, and its tip is at the tip of **r**.

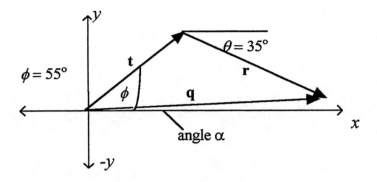

We can also draw so that the **r** and **t** vectors are reversed. We get the same thing for **q**.

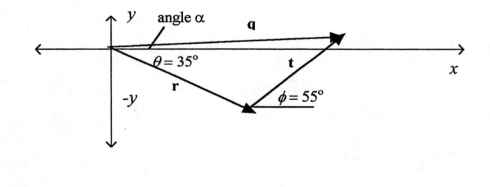

Vectors and Scalars Practice Problems

1. Dawn starts from zero, and bikes 2 km east, then 3 km west.
(a) Draw a vector diagram, and find her final position.

(b) Dawn starts from 0 again, but this time she goes 2 km north and the 3 km east. Draw a vector diagram, and find her final position.

2. Find the vector components of the vector q, if q = 3 cm, 30° from x to -y

3. Find the vector components of r = 10 m, 50° south of west.

4. Given the vectors A, B and C below sketch:

(a) A + B + C

(b) A + C - B

(c) B - C + A

5. Add a = 5 m/s, 30° south of east and b = 7 m/s, 20° west of north.

PHYSICS GRADE 11

Vectors and Scalars Practice Problem Solutions

1. *Dawn starts from zero, and bikes 2 km east, then 3 km west.*
(a) Draw a vector diagram, and find her final position.

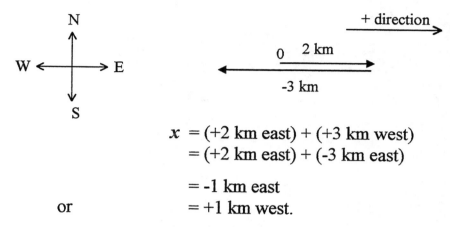

$$x = (+2 \text{ km east}) + (+3 \text{ km west})$$
$$= (+2 \text{ km east}) + (-3 \text{ km east})$$

$$= -1 \text{ km east}$$
or $\qquad = +1 \text{ km west.}$

(b) Dawn starts from 0 again, but this time she goes 2 km north and the 3 km east. Draw a vector diagram, and find her final position.

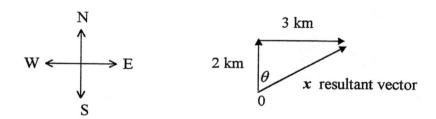

Use the Pythagorean theorem to find d:

$$d = \sqrt{(2 \text{ km})^2 + (3 \text{ km})^2} = \sqrt{13} \text{ km}$$

$$d = \textbf{3.6 km}$$

Find the angle θ:

$$\theta = \tan^{-1}\left(\frac{\text{opp}}{\text{adj}}\right) = \tan^{-1}\left(\frac{3}{2}\right) = \tan^{-1}(1.5) = \textbf{56}°$$

$d = 3.6$ km, $56°$ east of north.

2. *Find the vector components of the vector* **q**, *if q = 3 cm.*

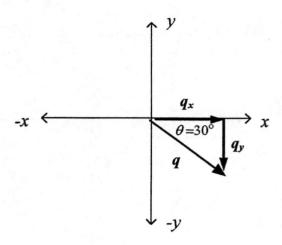

$$\sin\theta = \frac{\text{opp}}{\text{hyp}} = \frac{q_y}{q}$$

$$q_y = q\sin\theta$$

$$\quad\quad = (3 \text{ cm})\sin30° = 1.5 \text{ cm}$$

$$\cos\theta = \frac{\text{adj}}{\text{hyp}} = \frac{q_x}{q}$$

$$q_x = q\cos\theta$$

$$\quad\quad = (3 \text{ cm})\cos30° = 2.6 \text{ cm}$$

We have found $q_x = 2.6$ cm and $q_y = 1.5$ cm, so then

$$q_x = +2.6 \text{ cm (positive x direction)}$$

and $\quad\quad q_y = -1.5$ cm (negative y direction)

3. *Find the vector components of* **r** *= 10 m, 50° south of west.*

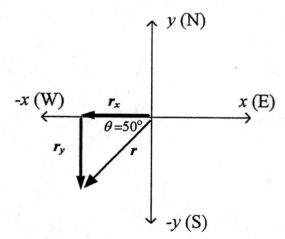

$$r_y = r\sin\theta = (10 \text{ m})\sin50° = 7.7 \text{ m}$$

$$r_x = r\cos\theta = (10 \text{ m})\cos50° = 6.4 \text{ m}$$

The components of **r** are:

$$r_x = -6.4 \text{ m}$$

$$r_y = -7.7 \text{ m}$$

4. *Given the vectors A, B and C below sketch:*

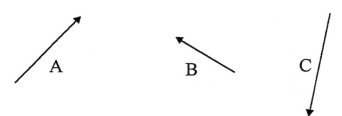

(a) A + B + C

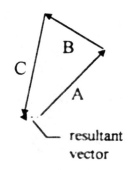

resultant vector

(b) A + C - B

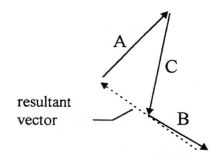

resultant vector

(c) B - C + A

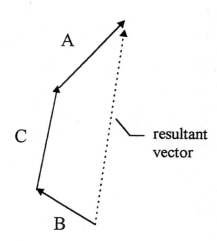

resultant vector

5. *Add* $a = 5$ m/s, $30°$ *south of east and* $b = 7$ m/s, $20°$ *west of north.*

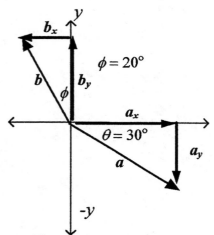

$a_x = a \cos\theta = (5 \text{ m/s}) \cos 30° = 4.3$ m/s

$b_x = b \sin\phi = (7 \text{ m/s}) \sin 20° = 2.4$ m/s

and

$a_y = a \sin\theta = (5 \text{ m/s}) \sin 30° = 2.5$ m/s

$b_y = b \cos\phi = (7 \text{ m/s}) \cos 20° = 6.6$ m/s

Vector	x component	y component
a	$a_x = +4.3$	$a_y = -2.5$
b	$b_x = -2.4$	$b_y = +6.6$
c	$c_x = a_x + b_x$ $= +4.3 + (-2.4)$ $= +1.9$ m/s	$c_y = a_y + b_y$ $= (-2.5) + (+6.6)$ $= +4.1$ m/s

Now we know that the resultant vector c has components

$c_x = +1.9$ m/s and $c_y = +4.1$ m/s.

We can find the magnitude of c using the Pythagorean theorem;

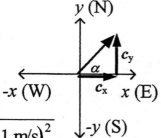

$$c = \sqrt{(c_x)^2 + (c_y)^2} = \sqrt{(1.9 \text{ m/s})^2 + (4.1 \text{ m/s})^2}$$

$= 4.5$ m/s is the magnitude of c.

Find the direction of c

$$\alpha = \tan^{-1}\left(\frac{\text{opp}}{\text{adj}}\right) = \tan^{-1}\left(\frac{c_y}{c_x}\right) = \tan^{-1}\left(\frac{4.1}{1.9}\right) = 65°$$

We now know that $c = $ **4.5 m/s, 65° north of east**.

Kinematics

Kinematics and dynamics are branches of mechanics. Mechanics describes how things move.

> **Mechanics** is the kind of physics that describes about how objects move. There are two branches of mechanics:
>
> **Kinematics** talks about how stuff moves without dealing with forces.
>
> **Dynamics** talks about how stuff moves by discussing forces, and how they cause motion

Displacement, Velocity and Acceleration

Displacement is the change in distance, Δd. It is the vector between initial location of an object and the final location of the object. The Δ is the symbol delta, and means 'the change in'. The delta symbol means that you take the final value of the quantity and subtract the initial value;

$\Delta d = d - d_o$, where d is the final location of the object and d_o (pronounced 'dee-naught') is the initial location of the object.

Average speed is the distance divided by the amount of time it took to go that distance. It is a scalar, since it has no direction. The equation for speed is;

$$\text{speed} = \frac{\text{distance}}{\text{time}}$$

Velocity, *is* a vector. There are two different kinds of velocity; average velocity and instantaneous velocity.

Average velocity is the total distance traveled divided by the total time it took to go that distance; the change in distance over the change in time, writen mathematically like;

$$\bar{v} = \frac{\Delta d}{\Delta t}$$

The bar over the *v* means that were talking about an average. The units for velocity are meters/second (m./s).

Example: *A cheetah runs 800m in 26 seconds in the positive x direction. What its the cat's average velocity in m/s ? in km/hour ?*

$$\bar{v} = \frac{\Delta d}{\Delta t} = \frac{+800 \text{ m}}{26 \text{ s}} = +30.8 \frac{\text{m}}{\text{s}}, \text{ in the x direction}$$

The cheetah runs +30.8 m/s in the x direction . Let's convert this to km/hour.

$$\bar{v} = \frac{+30.8 \text{ m}}{1 \text{ s}} \times 10^{-3} \frac{\text{km}}{\text{m}} \times 60 \frac{\text{s}}{\text{min}} \times 60 \frac{\text{min}}{\text{hour}}$$

$$= +30.8 \times 10^{-3} \times 60 \times 60 \frac{\text{km}}{\text{hour}}$$

$$= +111 \text{ km/hour, in the x direction.}$$

This is highway speed !

Instantaneous velocity is the velocity at an instant in time. What is the difference between average and instantaneous velocity ? Say you're in a car speeding up after a red light in a easternly direction. If you

---

look at the speedometer every few seconds, you'll see your velocity increase from 0 km/hour east, to 20 km/hour east, to 40 km/hour east... and so on. These velocities you're seeing every few seconds are *instantaneous* velocities; the velocity you are going when you happen to look at your speedometer. When use the word 'velocity', we usually mean instantaneous velocity.

Acceleration happens when the velocity changes. We usually think of acceleration as going faster. In physics, a velocity change could be speeding up, slowing down, or changing direction. These are all cases where there is acceleration. The **average acceleration** is;

$$\bar{a} = \frac{\Delta v}{\Delta t},$$

the change in velocity over the change in time is the average acceleration. The units for acceleration are meters/second² (m/s^2). Like with velocity, we usually talk about an **instantaneous acceleration**; when use the word 'acceleration', we usually mean instantaneous acceleration. **Deceleration** is the word for acceleration when something is slowing down.

Example: *A skater is going +10 m/s at t=0. Five seconds later, he's going +30 m/s. What is his average acceleration ?*

The skater's change in velocity from t=0 to t=5 is

$$\Delta v = v - v_o = +30 \text{ m} / \text{s} - (+10 \text{ m} / \text{s}) = +20 \text{ m} / \text{s},$$

so the average acceleration is;

$$\bar{a} = \frac{\Delta v}{\Delta t} = \frac{+20 \text{ m} / \text{s}}{5 \text{ s}} = +4 \frac{\text{m}}{\text{s}^2}$$

Graphs for 1-Dimensional Motion

The problems we've looked at so far are 1-dimensional. This means that the action happens in a straight line, like on the train, or the falling water balloon. One dimensional problems can be looked at a different way, using graphs. The best way to talk about these is with examples.

Position vs. Time graphs

Let's go rollerblading again. We start out at a constant velocity of +5 m/s, and travel for 400 seconds. At 400 seconds, we stop for 100 seconds, before turning around and bootin' it home at a velocity of -13m/s. We can plot a graph of this short trip. Remember that the x-axis is the horizontal (in this case the time) axis, and the y-axis is the vertical (distance) axis.

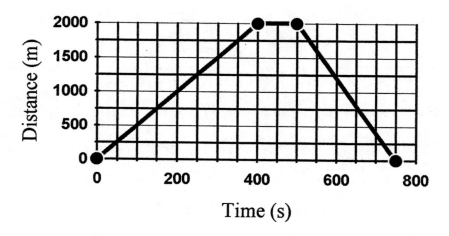

Position v.s Time for Rollerblade Trip

The first segment of the graph, between t=0 and t=400 s is when we were going +5 m/s. The segment between t=400 and t=500 is when we were stopped. The last segment between t=500 and t=750 s is when we headed back home. Now, if we didn't know how fast we were going, we could find out from the graph. We can do this by calculating the slope of the lines. The slope is defined as the change in y divided by the change in x;

$$\text{slope} = \frac{\Delta y}{\Delta x} = \frac{y_2 - y_1}{x_2 - x_1}.$$

For a distance vs. time graph, the slope is equal to the velocity, because the x-axis has time plotted, and the y-axis has distance plotted.

$$\text{slope} = \frac{\Delta y}{\Delta x} = \frac{\Delta d}{\Delta t} = \text{velocity}$$

To find the velocity of the first segment, we choose two points on the line. We'll use $x_1 = 100$ s, $y_1 = 500$ m, and $x_2 = 200$ s, $y_2 = 1000$ m. Points on a graph are usually written as coordinates, like (x_1, y_1). So the first point we chose is written (100, 500).

$$\text{velocity} = \text{slope} = \frac{\Delta y}{\Delta x} = \frac{y_2 - y_1}{x_2 - x_1} = \frac{1000 \text{ m} - 500 \text{ m}}{200 \text{ s} - 100 \text{ s}} = \frac{500 \text{ m}}{100 \text{ s}} = 5 \text{ m/s},$$

which is the same velocity as we had before. *A graph line going up means a positive slope and a positive velocity.* The second segment was when we were stopped;

$$\text{velocity} = \text{slope} = \frac{\Delta y}{\Delta x} = \frac{2000 \text{ m} - 2000 \text{ m}}{500 \text{ s} - 400 \text{ s}} = \frac{0 \text{ m}}{100 \text{ s}} = 0 \text{ m/s}$$

The velocity from the graph for the second segment is 0 m/s because our change in distance was zero. *A horizontal line means a zero slope and a*

---

zero velocity. The third segment was when we were heading back home. We'll again take a couple of points on the line. We'll use (500,2000) as point one, and (750,0) as point two. We have;

$$\text{velocity} = \text{slope} = \frac{\Delta y}{\Delta x} = \frac{0 \text{ m} - 2000 \text{ m}}{750 \text{ s} - 500 \text{ s}} = \frac{-2000}{150} \frac{\text{m}}{\text{s}} = -13 \text{ m / s,}$$

which is the same velocity as we said for the return trip. *A graph line going down means a negative slope and a negative velocity.*

What if we're not going at a constant velocity ? How does that change the graph ? We won't get a straight line anymore. This next graph is for a ball accelerating due to gravity, so a *constant* acceleration.

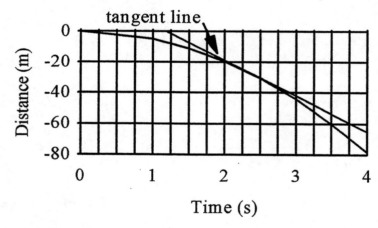

Position vs. Time for a Falling Ball

You can see that we now get a curved line (the distances are negative because the ball is falling in the negative direction). We can't find the slope of a curve, so to find the instantaneous velocity of the ball at a certain time, we have to draw a tangent line. I drew a tangent line on the graph at 2.5 s. It's a line that theoretically touches the graph at only one point; the point where we want to find the instantaneous velocity.

Since the tangent line is a straight line, we can find its slope. We'll use points (2.5,-30) and (3.75,-60),

$$\text{inst. velocity} = \text{slope} = \frac{\Delta y}{\Delta x} = \frac{-60 \text{ m} - (-30) \text{ m}}{3.75 \text{ s} - 2.5 \text{ s}} = \frac{-30 \text{ m}}{1.25 \text{ s}} = -24 \text{ m/s}$$

is the instantaneous velocity of the ball at 2.5 s.

Velocity vs. Time Graphs

What if we plot velocity vs. time for the falling ball ? How will the line look then ? It looks like this,

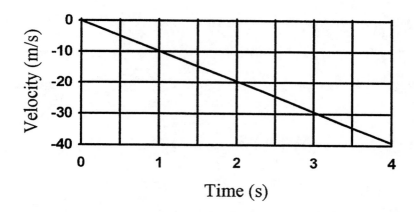

Velocity vs. Time for Falling Ball

(The velocities are negative because the ball is falling in the negative direction) The slope of a velocity vs. time graph is the acceleration, because;

$$\text{slope} = \frac{\Delta y}{\Delta x} = \frac{\Delta v}{\Delta t} = \text{acceleration}$$

We can now find the acceleration of our freely falling ball from the graph.

$$\text{acceleration} = m = \frac{\Delta y}{\Delta x} = \frac{-35 \text{ m/s} - (-10) \text{ m/s}}{3.5 \text{ s} - 1 \text{ s}} = \frac{-25 \text{ m/s}}{2.5 \text{ s}} = -10 \text{ m/s}^2$$

this is very close to the value for $g = -9.80$ m/s^2 we mentioned earlier. It's not exactly the same because reading from graphs can be kind of inaccurate. This is because we have to estimate the location of the points we're using to calculate the slope.

> A distance vs. time graph is **linear** (a straight line) if the velocity is **uniform** (constant).
> A velocity vs. time graph is linear if the acceleration is uniform.

An easy way to find the distance the ball has fallen is to count the number of squares between the graph and the x-axis. This is "the area under the graph". There are 16 complete squares (piecing together the partial squares) between the graph and the x-axis. We need to multiply by the time for each square on the x-axis, and the velocity for each square on the y-axis:

each square on the x-axis represents 0.5 s of time.

each square on the y-axis represents -10 m/s of velocity.

We multiply these together and get 0.5 s x -10 m/s $= -5$ m (the seconds cancel). Each square between represents -5 m of distance covered. If we multiply this by the number of squares between the graph and the x-axis, we get *the total distance the ball has fallen*: -5 m x 16 = -80 m. The ball fell -80 m. The negative just means that the ball fell *down*.

> The **area** between the graph and the x-axis of the velocity vs. time graph is the distance traveled.

Another useful thing to know is that the line will cross the y-axis at the value of the initial velocity. In the graph above, the initial velocity is zero, since the line cross the y-axis at zero. What if we started to ball with an initial velocity of -5 m/s ? The graph would look like this;

Velocity vs. Time for Falling Ball

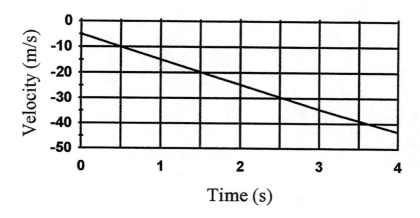

the line crosses the y-axis at -5 m/s. When we think about the kinematics equations we looked at, this makes sense. We already showed from the definition of slope that $a = \dfrac{\Delta v}{\Delta t}$, which is the same as

$$a = \frac{(v - v_o)}{(t - t_o)}$$

or $\qquad (v - v_o) = a(t - t_o)$

We can see that we started at $t_o = 0$, so the equation is;

$$(v - v_o) = at$$

or $\qquad v = v_o + at$.

This is the equation that we discussed earlier in the kinematics equation section, and we just got the same thing using the definition for slope. At least we're being consistent.

PHYSICS GRADE 11

Kinematics in One-Dimension

In this section, we're going to look at some equations we can use for *motion in one direction, and constant acceleration*. These are very important limitations on these equations.

The kinematic equations are;

$$v = v_o + at$$

$$d = \frac{1}{2}(v_o + v)t$$

$$d = v_o t + \frac{1}{2}at^2$$

$$v^2 = v_o^2 + 2ad$$

where ; t = time that has passed since $t_o = 0$
$\quad\quad\quad d$ = displacement (distance travelled) during time t
$\quad\quad\quad v$ = final velocity, at time t
$\quad\quad\quad v_o$ = initial velocity, at time $t_o = 0$
$\quad\quad\quad a$ = acceleration, which is always a constant

Let's use a couple of these to solve problems;

Example: *A Zoracian anti-gravity spaceship is looking for some humans to abduct. The pilot is cruising over some fields at a velocity of 40 m/s, when it sees a suitable candidate 300 m ahead. If the ship accelerates at a rate of 25 m/s², (a) how fast will the ship be going when it swoops down on its victim ? (b) How long will it take ?*

We'll call the direction in which the Zoracians are travelling the positive direction. The first thing we do, is figure out what information we have. We know;

$$v_o = +40 \text{ m/s}$$
$$d = +300 \text{ m}$$
$$a = +25 \text{ m/s}^2$$

initial velocity v_o = +40 m/s
distance d = +300 m
acceleration a = +25 m/s²

One we know what we have, it's easier to figure out what equation will give us what we want.

(a) We can use the equation $v^2 = v_o^2 + 2ad$ to find the final velocity, since we know v_o, d, and a.

$$v^2 = v_o^2 + 2ad$$
$$= (+40 \text{ m/s})^2 + 2\,(+25 \text{ m/s}^2)(+300 \text{ m})$$
$$= +1600\,(\text{m/s})^2 + 7500\,(\text{m/s})^2$$
$$= +9100\,(\text{m/s})^2$$

so $\quad v = \pm 95 \text{ m/s}$

Mathematically, we get both +95 m/s and -95 m/s, since the sqaure of both of these will give us +9100 (m/s)². We have to decide which one is the right answer depending on the situation. In our example, the ship is accelerating in the positive direction, so we would have a positive final velocity.

The ship will be travelling at +95 m/s when it reaches its victim. Notice that the units worked out to be the right ones for velocity. If they didn't, we know we made a mistake somewhere.

(b) To find the time it takes to reach the human, we can use the final velocity we just calculated in (a), in either equation $d = \frac{1}{2}(v_o + v)t$ or $v = v_o + at$. We'll rearange the second one to solve for t.

$$at = v - v_o$$
$$t = (v - v_o)/a$$
$$= \frac{(+95\,\text{m}/\text{s} - (+40\,\text{m}/\text{s}))}{+25\,\text{m}/\text{s}^2}$$
$$= 2.2\,\text{s}$$

The Zoracians will be in position to snatch up the human in 2.2 seconds.

In this example, the human was stationary with respect to the ship. If the human were runing, we have to treat it a bit differently. The motion of the two objects can be interrelated. The next example looks at two moving objects.

PHYSICS GRADE 11

> **Example:** *Sharon is on a train travelling at 90 km/hr. An avid runnner, she is annoying the other passengers by running back and forth on the train at a speed of 10 km/hr. (a) What is her velocity relative to the Earth in each direction ? (b) The train starts to decelerate at a rate of 200 km/hr² at t=0 when she's running east. If she runs for another 0.1 hours, what is her final velocity, relative to the Earth.*

We'll call the direction of the train's velocity positive east.

$$v_{train} = +90 \text{ km/hour, east}$$

⟶

(a) We know ; $v_{train} = +90$ km/hour east, relative to the Earth

Sharon running east: $v_{S\,train} = +10$ km/hour east, relative to the train

Sharon running west: $v_{S\,train} = +10$ km/hour west, relative to train
     or $= -10$ km/hour east, relative to train

To find Sharon's velocity with respect to the Earth, we add the velocities in the east direction;

$$v_{S\,Earth} = v_{train} + v_{S\,train},$$

so when she's running east,

$$v_{S\,Earth} = +90 \text{ km/hr} + (+10 \text{ km/hr})$$
$$= +100 \text{ km/hr, east}$$

and when she's running west,

$$v_{S\,Earth} = +90 \text{ km/hr} + (-10 \text{ km/hr})$$
$$= +80 \text{ km/hr, east}$$

When Sharon is running east on the train, her velocity is +100 km/hr, east, and when she's running west on the train, it's +80 km/hr, east relative to the Earth.

(b) We know that Sharon's initial velocity relative to the Earth is

$$v_{S\ Earth} = v_o = +100 \text{ km/hr, east}$$

$$t = 0.1 \text{ hours}$$

and that the train is decelerating 0.1 km/hr². Recall that is something is decelerating, it's acceleration is in the opposite direction of it's velocity, so

$$v_{S\ Earth} = +100 \text{ km/hour, east}$$

$$a = +200 \text{ km/hour}^2, \text{ west}$$

$$a = +200 \text{ km/hr}^2, \text{ west}$$

$$\text{or} \qquad = -200 \text{ km/hr}^2, \text{ east.}$$

We now have all the information we need to find her final velocity with respect to the Earth. We can use the kinematic equation;

$$v = v_o + at$$

$$v = +100 \text{ km/hr} + (-200 \text{ km/hr}^2)(0.1 \text{ hr})$$

$$= +80 \text{ km/hr, east}$$

Sharon's final velocity is +80 km/hr, east, relative to the earth.

We sometimes want to know how it long it takes something to drop due to gravity if we let it go from a height. This kind of object is called a *freely falling body*, and we say that its acceleration is the *acceleration due to gravity*. The acceleration due to gravity is a constant on the planet equal to 9.80 m/s² near the Earth's surface. We use the symbol '**g**' for the acceleration due to gravity, and $g = -9.80$ m/s².

We usually call 'down' negative in freely falling body problems, so **g** is usually negative. Since gravity is constant acceleration, we can use the kinematic equations we just saw for freely falling bodies.

We have all seen that somethings fall faster than others if we drop them from a height. If I were to drop a physics20 test and an anvil from the top of the school, we would all see that the anvil hit the ground first. This has nothing to do with **g**, or with how heavy things are. The reason the anvil hits sooner is because of *air resistance* (the molecules in the air pushing against the falling body). Different shaped objects react have different effects from air resistance. You've seen this yourself when you try to throw a paper airplane. If you throw it flat side first, it doesn't go anywhere. You throw it pointed side first because it's more *aerodynamic*, it reduces the amount of air resitance. On the moon there are very few molecules floating around in the atmosphere. In 1971, when astronaut David Scott dropped a hammer and a feather at the same on the moon, he saw they hit the lunar surface at exactly the same time. My point here is that how fast something falls has ***nothing*** to do with how much it weighs.

For the most part, we ignore the effects of air resitance in problems.

Example: *We drop a water ballon from a second story window (say 20 meters from the ground). If it starts at rest (zero initial velocity), what is the final velocity and how long will it take to hit Kathryn's head if she is 1.6 m tall ?*

We're going to draw a picture first.

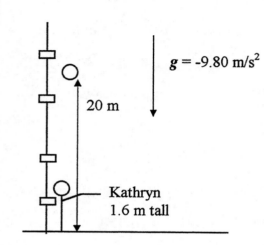

We know;

$$v_o = 0$$

$$a = g = +9.80 \text{ m/s}^2$$

$$d = 20 \text{ m} - 1.6 \text{ m}$$

$$= 18.4 \text{ m}$$

We can use $v^2 = v_o{}^2 + 2ad$ to find the final velocity.

$$v^2 = v_o{}^2 + 2ad$$
$$= 0 + 2(-9.80\text{m/s}^2)(18.4 \text{ m})$$
$$= 360 \text{ (m/s)}^2$$

so $v = -19.0$ m/s, since the velocity is in the negative direction

To determine how long it takes, we can use the final velocity we just found in equation $v = v_o + at$. Remember that the initial velocity is zero, so

$$v = at$$
$$t = v/a$$
$$= (-19.0 \text{ m/s})/(-9.80 \text{ m/s}^2)$$
$$= 1.94 \text{ s}$$

The velocity of the water baloon is -19 m/s as it hits Kathryn, and it takes 1.94 seconds to reach her.

PHYSICS GRADE 11

Kinematics in Two-Dimensions

It's pretty obvious what the limitations are of one-dimensional kinematics; we don't usually move in one-dimension. We throw things in arcs and drive over bumps to get stuff where we want. Fortunately, the physics we need to use for two-dimensional kinematics is the same we used for one-dimensional motion (the only difference is that we now *really* need all the trigonometry and vector stuff).

Remember that every vector is made up of two vector components, and that we can easily add the vectors in each direction ? If not, peek at it again... this comes in handy soon. All we do for two-dimension motion is break the velocity, acceleration, and displacement vectors up in their x and y-components. This way we have two one-dimensional problems that we can solve separtely using the one-dimensional kinematic equation we already know. We do change the notation a bit, so that we always know which direction we're working on.

Remember the one-dimensional kinematics equations are;

$$v = v_o + at$$

$$d = \frac{1}{2}(v_o + v)t$$

$$d = v_o t + \frac{1}{2}at^2$$

$$v^2 = v_o{}^2 + 2ad$$

PHYSICS GRADE 11

x-component	y-component
$v_x = v_{ox} + a_x t$	$v_y = v_{oy} + a_y t$
$x = \dfrac{1}{2}(v_{ox} + v_x)t$	$y = \dfrac{1}{2}(v_{oy} + v_y)t$
$x = v_{ox}t + \dfrac{1}{2}a_x t^2$	$y = v_{oy}t + \dfrac{1}{2}a_y t^2$
$v_x^2 = v_{ox}^2 + 2a_x x$	$v_y^2 = v_{oy}^2 + 2a_y y$

The only difference between the one and two-dimensional equations is the subscripts. Notice that t is the same for both of the sets of equations, since time is a scalar.

    I think a few examples will help here.

Example: *A gnat flying through the air has a $v_{ox} = +0.3$ m/s, $v_{oy} = -0.1$ m/s, $a_{ox} = +0.1$ m/s^2, and $a_{oy} = +0.05$ m/s^2. After 20 s, what is the velocity of the gnat ?*

We *always* (unless otherwise told) assume that the motion begins at $t = 0$ in the $x = 0$, $y = 0$ position.

We'll play with the x-direction first. We know; $v_{ox} = +0.3$ m/s
$$a_x = +0.1 \text{ m/s}^2$$
$$t = 20 \text{ s}$$

we can find the final x direction velocity by using;

$$v_x = v_{ox} + a_x t$$
$$v_x = (+0.3 \text{ m/s}) + (+0.1 \text{ m/s}^2)(20 \text{ s})$$
$$= +2.3 \text{ m/s}$$

---

for the y-direction we know;

$$v_{oy} = -0.1 \text{ m/s}$$

$$a_y = +0.05 \text{ m/s}^2$$

$$t = 20 \text{ s}$$

and we can find the final y direction velocity the same way;

$$v_y = v_{oy} + a_y t$$
$$v_y = (-0.1 \text{ m/s}) + (+0.05 \text{ m/s}^2)(20 \text{ s})$$
$$= +0.9 \text{ m/s}$$

We use the Pythagorean theorem to find the magnitude of the final velocity, v:

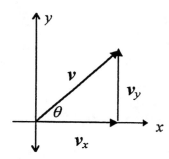

$$v = \sqrt{v_x^2 + v_y^2}$$

$$v = \sqrt{(+2.3 \text{ m/s})^2 + (+0.9 \text{ m/s})^2}$$

$$v = \sqrt{5.29(\text{m/s})^2 + 0.81(\text{m/s})^2}$$

$$v = 2.5 \text{ m/s}$$

and finally, we find the direction using the inverse tangent function;

$$\theta = tan^{-1}\left(\frac{v_y}{v_x}\right) = tan^{-1}\left(\frac{+0.9}{+2.3}\right) = 21.4°$$

So the final velocity of the gnat is 2.5 m/s 21.4° above the positive x-axis.

The next couple of examples are **projectile motion** problems. A projectile is basically something flying through the air. In this kind of problem, we have acceleration due to gravity working in the y direction, and no acceleration in the x direction. What this means is that we have a constant velocity in the x-direction, so $v_{ox} = v_x$. This turns out to be very handy. The next examples might help make this make sense.

Example: *We're going to throw a water balloon at Kathryn again. Of course, she's learned not to walk directly under the window, so we have to have it land on her head 10 meters away from the building. To do this, we have to give the balloon an initial horizontal velocity. I've drawn a picture below with all the information we need. Find the time it takes to hit Kathryn, and the initial horizontal velocity and final horizontal and vertical velocities of the balloon.*

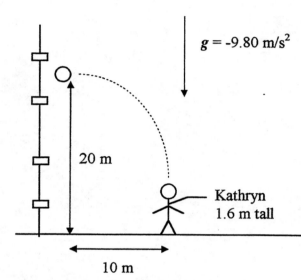

For projectile motion problems, we can use the fact that there's gravity accelerating the body in the y direction. Another important thing to realize is that once the balloon is thrown, there's nothing to make the velocity in the x direction change (since we ignore air resistance), so *we have constant velocity in the x direction.* Since we know the distance and acceleration in the y direction, we'll use this to find the time it takes to fall. We can use;

$$y = v_{oy}t + \frac{1}{2}a_y t^2 = \frac{1}{2}a_y t^2$$, since the initial vertical velocity is

zero. Remember that $y = (-20\text{m}) + (+1.6 \text{ m}) = -18.4$ m, because of Kathryn's height. So,

$$2y = a_y t^2$$

$$t = \sqrt{\frac{2y}{a_y}}$$

$$t = \sqrt{\frac{2(-18.4 \text{ m})}{-9.80 \text{ m}/\text{s}^2}} = \sqrt{3.76 \text{ s}^2} = 1.94 \text{ s}$$

and the final vertical velocity can be now be found with

$$v_y = a_y\, t$$
$$= (-9.80 \text{ m/s}^2)(1.94 \text{ s})$$
$$= -19.0 \text{ m/s}$$

We know the balloon will reach Kathryn's head after 1.94 seconds with a y direction velocity of -19 m/s.

Now to find the velocity in the x direction. Remember that *since there is no acceleration in the x direction, the initial and final horizontal velocities are the same.*

$$v_{0x} = v_x = \frac{x}{t}$$

$$= \frac{+10 \text{ m}}{1.94 \text{ s}} = +5.2 \text{ m/s}$$

We now know that we have to give the balloon a horizontal (x direction) velocity of +5.2 m/s.

Example: *A player kicks a football with an initial velocity of 16 m/s, 30°
above the ground. How high will the ball go, and how far from, the
player will it land ?*

Let's draw a picture.

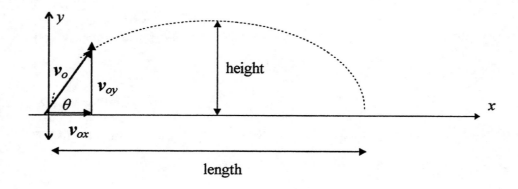

We have to find the x and y components of the initial velocity first;

$$v_{ox} = v_o \, cos\theta$$

$$= (16 \text{ m/s}) \, cos30° = +13.8 \text{ m/s}$$

$$v_{oy} = v_o \, sin\theta$$

$$= (16 \text{ m/s}) \, sin30° = +8.0 \text{ m/s}$$

like we did before, we calculate the time using the y component. In this
case, the ball has an initial velocity in the y direction, but we know that
eventually the ball has to reach its highest point, when the $v_y = 0$. When $v_y
= 0$, we the ball has travelled 1/2 of its horizontal path, and taken 1/2 of
the total time for the trip. So 1/2 the time is

$$v_y = v_{oy} + a_y \, t_{1/2}$$

$$t_{1/2} = \frac{v_y - v_{oy}}{a_y} = \frac{0 \text{ m/s} - 8.0 \text{ m/s}}{-9.80 \text{ m/s}^2} = 0.82 \text{ s}$$

$$t = 2 \times t_{1/2} = 2 \times 0.82 \text{ s} = 1.63 \text{ s}$$

The time it takes for the ball to get to its highest point is 0.82 s, and the time for the whole trip is 1.63 s. Now we'll find the height and distance the ball goes. We'll find height using

$$v_y^2 = v_{oy}^2 + 2a_y y$$

so
$$y = \frac{v_y^2 - v_{oy}^2}{2a_y} = \frac{(0 \text{ m/s})^2 - (8.0 \text{ m/s})^2}{2(-9.80 \text{ m/s}^2)} = 3.3 \text{ m}$$

The ball reaches a height of 3.3 m.

We'll find the distance it travels in the x direction using

$$v_{0x} = v_x = \frac{x}{t}$$

$$= v_x \, t$$

$$= (+13.8 \text{ m/s})(1.63 \text{ s}) = +22.5 \text{ m}$$

The ball lands +22.5 m away from the player.

We talked about relative velocity in one dimension (that was when our fitness enthusiast, Sharon, was running on the train). We can do the same kind of thing in two dimensions, like in the next example.

Example: *Boaters often have to know how fast a river is flowing to land at a particular point on the other riverbank. Marc knows that he can paddle at a rate of 3 m/s, relative to the water, and the river flows at a rate of 10 m/s, and is 30 m wide. (a) If he wants to land at the dock on the other side, how far upstream from the dock does he have to start if he paddles only in the y direction ? (b) What is his velocity relative to the shore while he's canoeing across ?*

As usual, a picture comes in handy.

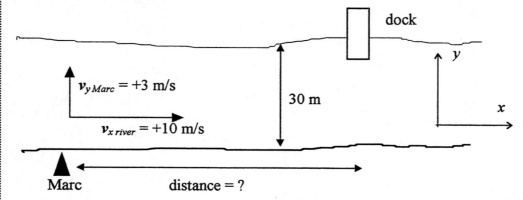

Since the river is flowing at a rate of +10 m/s, Marc's canoe will be pulled along by the river while he is canoeing straight across.

We know *relative to the shore*; $v_{x\ river\ S} = $ constant $ = +10$ m/s

$$v_{y\ river\ S} = 0 \text{ m/s}$$

relative to the water; $v_{y\ Marc\ W} = $ constant $ = +3$ m/s

$$y = +30 \text{ m}$$

(a) The first thing we have to find out is how long it takes him to go across the river (in the y direction), then we can use that time in the x direction to find out how far downstream the river pulls him.

$$t = \frac{y}{v_y} = \frac{+30 \text{ m}}{+3 \text{ m} / \text{s}} = 10 \text{ s}$$

the distance Marc is pulled downstream in 10 seconds is;

$$x = v_x \ t$$

$$= (+10 \text{ m/s})(10 \text{ s}) = +100 \text{ m, relative to the}$$
shore

Marc has to start 100 m upstream to land at the dock.

(b) We have to add the veloctiy of the river, relative to the shore, to the velocity of Marc, relative to the water, for each component.

$$v_{x \, Marc \, S} \quad = v_{x \, Marc \, W} + v_{x \, Water \, S}$$

$$= (0 \text{ m/s}) + (+10 \text{ m/s}) = +10 \text{ m/s, relative to the}$$
shore

$$v_{y \, Marc \, S} \quad = v_{y \, Marc \, W} + v_{y \, Water \, S}$$

$$= (+3 \text{ m/s}) + (0 \text{ m/s}) = +3 \text{ m/s, relative to the shore}$$

We use the Pythagorean theorem to find the magnitude of the final velocity $v_{Marc \, S}$;

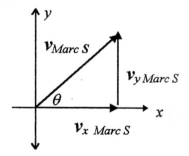

$$v_{Marc \, S} = \sqrt{v_{x \, Marc \, S}{}^2 + v_{y \, Marc \, S}{}^2}$$

$$v_{Marc \, S} = \sqrt{(+10 \text{ m/s})^2 + (+3 \text{ m/s})^2}$$

$$v_{Marc \, S} = \sqrt{100(\text{m/s})^2 + 9(\text{m/s})^2}$$

$$v_{Marc \, S} = 10.4 \text{ m/s}$$

and finally, we find the direction using the inverse tangent function;

$$\theta = tan^{-1}\left(\frac{v_{y \, Marc \, S}}{v_{x \, Marc \, S}}\right) = tan^{-1}\left(\frac{+3}{+10}\right) = 16.7°$$

Marc's velocity relative to the shore is is 10.4 m/s 16.7° above the positive x-axis.

PHYSICS GRADE 11

Kinematics Practice Problems

1. A jet flies 1000 m east in 5 seconds. Then returns to its starting point. On the return trip, it flies the distance in 4 seconds.
(a) What were the average velocities for each trip ?

(b) The same jet flew for 6 s with an average velocity of -270 m/s. How far did it fly ?

(c) The jet starts at 10 m/s, and goes to 200 m/s in 10 s. What is its acceleration ?

(d) The jet now slows down from 200 m/s to 30 m/s in 12 s. What is the acceleration ?

2. This is a graph of a duck flying in one-dimension (east and west). East

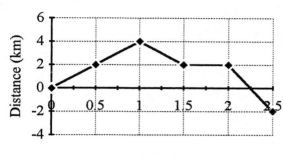

Distance vs. Time

is positive.

(a) Describe the motion of the duck's flight.

(b) What is the duck's velocity during hours 2 to 2.5 ?

3. A car starts at 0 m/s, and accelerates for 2 minutes. It hen travels at a constant velocity for 5 minutes, then decelerates for 3 minutes until it's stopped again.

(a) Sketch the graph of the car's motion.

(b) If the constant velocity it reaches is 1 km/min., what is the acceleration between 0 and 2 minutes ? Between 7 and 10 minutes ?

(c) Determine graphically how far the car traveled.

4. A motorcycle accelerates at 3 m/s^2. Its initial velocity is -6 m/s.
(a) How fast is it going after 2 s ?

(b) How far did it go ?

5. How long would it take a skater to pass a stationary post if the post is 10 m away, and the skater accelerates from 0 m/s at a rate of 2 m/s^2 ?

(b) How long does it take if $v_o = +2.5$ m/s ?

6. We throw a ball at the ground with an initial speed of 3.2 m/s, and it takes 3 seconds to hit the ground. How far does it fall ?

7. I let go of a piece of bread from a balcony. A bird flying 5 m overhead sees me drop it, and starts to dive straight down toward the bread the instant I release it. She catches it after it has fallen 3 m. Assuming she accelerated constantly ($v_o = 0$) from the time I let go, what was her acceleration ?

8. A ball starts from rest and accelerates. The eastward component of the acceleration is +0.4 m/s^2, and the northward component is -0.2 m/s^2. What is the final velocity of the ball after 10 seconds ?

9. I throw a baseball in the air with an initial velocity of 11 m/s at an angle of 50° from the ground.

(a) How long is it in the air before another person catches it (they catch it at the same level that it left my hand) ?

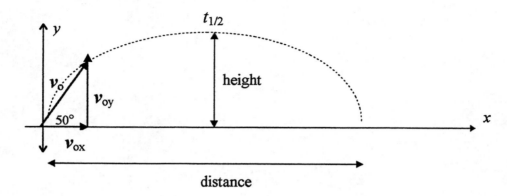

9.(b) How far does the ball go ?

10. A plane drops a package from 1000 m above the ground. It's going +90 m/s when the package is released.
(a) What's the horizontal distance (d_x) the package travels before it hits the ground ?

10. (b) What is the final velocity on impact ?

11. A plane is flying +900 km/hr west. A 30 km/hr wind, coming from the north-east kicks in. What speed and direction must the pilot change to in order to keep going +900 km/hr relative to the ground ?

PHYSICS GRADE 11

Kinematics Practice Problem Solutions

*1. A jet flies 1000m east in 5 seconds. Then returns to its starting point.
On the return trip, it flies the distance in 4 seconds.
(a) What were the average velocities for each trip ?*

We'll call east the positive x direction.

Eastbound trip: $\bar{v} = \dfrac{\Delta d}{\Delta t} = \dfrac{+1000 \text{ m}}{5 \text{ s}} = $ **+200 m/s**

Return trip: $\bar{v} = \dfrac{\Delta d}{\Delta t} = \dfrac{-1000 \text{ m}}{4 \text{ s}} = $ **-250 m/s**

(b) The same jet flew for 6 s with an average velocity of -270 m/s. How far did it fly ?

We use the same equation, but rearrange it to solve for distance:

$$\Delta d = \bar{v} \, \Delta t = (-270 \text{ m/s})(6 \text{ s}) = \textbf{-1620 m}$$

(c) The jet starts at 10 m/s, and goes to 200 m/s in 10 s. What is its acceleration ?

The change in velocity from $t = 0$ to $t = 10$ is

$$\Delta v = v - v_o = (200 \text{ m/s}) - (10 \text{ m/s}) = +190 \text{ m/s}$$

so the average acceleration is

$$\bar{a} = \dfrac{\Delta v}{\Delta t} = \dfrac{+190 \text{ m/s}}{10 \text{ s}} = \textbf{-19 m/s}^2.$$

(d) The jet now slows down from 200 m/s to 30 m/s in 12 s. What is the acceleration ?

$$\bar{a} = \dfrac{\Delta v}{\Delta t} = \dfrac{v - v_o}{\Delta t} = \dfrac{(+30 \text{ m/s}) - (+200 \text{ m/s})}{12 \text{ s}} = \dfrac{(-190 \text{ m/s})}{12 \text{ s}} = \textbf{-14 m/s}^2.$$

2. *This is a graph of a duck flying in one-dimension (east and west). East*

Distance vs. Time

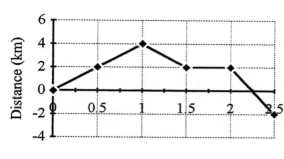

is positive.

(a) Describe the motion of the duck's flight.

From 0 to 1 hours, the duck is flying at a constant velocity east, for 4 km.

From 1 to 1.5 hours, the duck is flying west at a constant velocity, for 2 km.

From 1.5 to 2 hours, the duck is stopped, 2 km east of the starting point.

From 2 to 2.5 hours, the duck is again flying west for 4 km , at a greater velocity than before.

(b) What is the duck's velocity during hours 2 to 2.5 ?

$$\text{velocity} = \text{slope} = \frac{\Delta y}{\Delta x} = \frac{y_2 - y_1}{x_2 - x_1} = \frac{-2 \text{ km} - (+2 \text{ km})}{2.5 \text{ hr} - 2 \text{ hr}} = \frac{-4}{0.5} \frac{\text{km}}{\text{hr}} = \textbf{-8 km/hr}$$

3. *A car starts at 0 m/s, and accelerates for 2 minutes. It hen travels at a constant velocity for 5 minutes, then decelerates for 3 minutes until it's stopped again.*

(a) Sketch the graph of the car's motion.

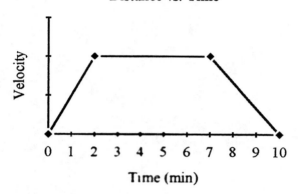

Distance vs. Time

(b) If the constant velocity it reaches is 1 km/min., what is the acceleration between 0 and 2 minutes ? Between 7 and 10 minutes ?

Sketch the graph and find the slope of the lines.

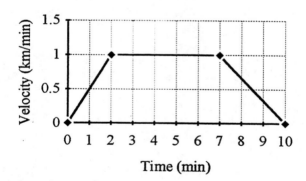

Distance vs. Time

Between 0 and 2 minutes:

$$\text{acceleration} = \frac{\Delta y}{\Delta x} = \frac{1 \text{ km/min} - 0 \text{ km/min}}{2 \text{ min} - 0 \text{ min}} = \frac{+1}{2} \frac{\text{km/min}}{\text{min}} = +0.5 \text{ km/min}^2$$

Between 7 and 10 minutes:

$$\text{acceleration} = \frac{\Delta y}{\Delta x} = \frac{0 \text{ km/min} - 1 \text{ km/min}}{10 \text{ min} - 7 \text{ min}} = \frac{-1}{3} \frac{\text{km/min}}{\text{min}} = -0.33 \text{ km/min}^2$$

(c) Determine graphically how far the car traveled.

We can do this by counting the squares.

y-axis : 2 squares = 1 km/min., so 1 square = 0.5 km/min.

x-axis : 1 square = 1 min.

Each square = 0.5 km/min. x 1 min. = 0.5 km

We multiply this by the number of squares between the graph and the x-axis. I counted about 15 squares:

0.5 km x 15 squares = 7.5 km

The distance traveled is 7.5 km.

4. A motorcycle accelerates at 3 m/s². Its initial velocity is -6 m/s.
(a) How fast is it going after 2 s ?

We know $\quad$ $a = +3$ m/s^2
$\qquad\qquad$ $v_o = -6$ m/s
$\qquad\qquad$ $t = 1$ s
$\qquad\qquad$ $v = ?$

Use $\qquad$ $v = v_o + at$

$\qquad\qquad$ $= -6$ m/s $+ (+3$ m/s$^2)(1$ s$)$

$\qquad$ $v = $ **-3 m/s** (the acceleration is in the opposite

direction of the velocity, so the motorcycle slows down.)

(b) How far did it go ?

Use $\qquad$ $d = \dfrac{1}{2}(v_o + v)t$

$\qquad\qquad$ $= \dfrac{1}{2}(-6$ m/s $- 3$ m/s$)(1$ s$)$

so $\qquad$ $d = $ **-4.5 m**

---

5. *How long would it take a skater to pass a stationary post if the post is 10 m away, and the skater accelerates from 0 m/s at a rate of 2 m/s² ?*

We know $a = +2$ m/s²
      $v_0 = 0$ m/s
      $d = 10$ m
      $t = ?$

We can use $d = v_0 t + \dfrac{1}{2}at^2 = \dfrac{1}{2}at^2$, since $v_0 = 0$ m/s.

so $t = \sqrt{\dfrac{2d}{a}} = \sqrt{\dfrac{2(10\text{ m})}{(2\text{ m/s}^2)}} = \textbf{3.2 s}$

(b) How long does it take if $v_o = +2.5$ m/s ?

We know $a = +2$ m/s²
      $v_0 = +2.5$ m/s
      $d = 10$ m
      $t = ?$

It's harder to use $d = v_0 t + \dfrac{1}{2}at^2$, since $v_0 \neq 0$ m/s. We'll first find the final velocity, v using

$$v^2 = v_0{}^2 + 2ad$$

$$= (+2.5 \text{ m/s})^2 + 2(+2 \text{ m/s}^2)(10 \text{ m})$$

$$= 46.3 \text{ m}^2/\text{s}^2$$

so $v = +6.8$ m/s

(we know the skater is going in the positive direction, because the initial velocity is positive)

Now we can use $v = v_0 + at$ to find the time it takes.

$$t = \frac{v - v_0}{a} = \frac{+6.8 \text{ m/s} - (+2.5 \text{ m/s})}{+2 \text{ m/s}^2}$$

$$t = \textbf{2.2 s}$$

6. *We throw a ball at the ground with an initial speed of 3.2 m/s, and it takes 3 seconds to hit the ground. How far does it fall ?*

It keeps accelerating due to gravity.

Down is the negative direction.

We know $a = g = -9.81 \text{ m/s}^2$

$v_0 = -3.2 \text{ m/s}$ (negative because it's directed down)

$t = 3 \text{ s}$

$d = ?$

We can use $d = v_0 t + \dfrac{1}{2} at^2$

$= (-3.2 \text{ m/s})(3 \text{ s}) + \dfrac{1}{2}(-9.81 \text{ m/s}^2)(3 \text{ s})^2$

$d = \textbf{-54 m}$ (negative since the ball fell *down*)

---

7. *I let go of a piece of bread from a balcony. A bird flying 5 m overhead sees me drop it, and starts to dive straight down toward the bread the instant I release it. She catches it after it has fallen 3 m. Assuming she accelerated constantly ($v_o = 0$) from the time I let go, what was her acceleration ?*

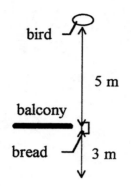

bird

5 m

balcony

bread   3 m

In the time it took her to dive from 10 m above the balcony edge to 3 m below the balcony edge, the bread fell (under the influence of gravity) 3 m. We can figure out how long she accelerated by finding out how long it took the bread to fall.

the time for bread to fall:
$$a = -9.81 \text{ m/s}^2$$
$$v_o = 0 \text{ m/s}$$
$$d = -3 \text{ m}$$
$$t = ?$$

$$d = v_o t + \frac{1}{2} at^2 = \frac{1}{2} at^2 \text{ , since } v_o = 0 \text{ m/s.}$$

so
$$t = \sqrt{\frac{2d}{a}} = \sqrt{\frac{2(-3 \text{ m})}{(-9.81 \text{ m/s}^2)}} = \mathbf{0.8 \text{ s}}$$

Now we know it took 0.8 s for the bird to fly down $-5 \text{ m} + (-3 \text{ m}) = -8 \text{ m}$

from rest, so
$$v_o = 0 \text{ m/s}$$

$$d = -8 \text{ m}$$
$$t = 0.8 \text{ s}$$
$$a = ?$$

$$d = v_o t + \frac{1}{2} at^2 = \frac{1}{2} at^2 \text{ , since } v_o = 0 \text{ m/s.}$$

so
$$a = \frac{2d}{t^2} = \frac{2(-8 \text{ m})}{(0.8 \text{ s})^2} = \mathbf{-25 \text{ m/s}^2, \text{ down}}$$

8. *A ball starts from rest and accelerates. The eastward component of the acceleration is +0.4 m/s², and the northward component is -0.2 m/s². What is the final velocity of the ball after 10 seconds ?*

Find the final velocity of the x-component (eastward) first:

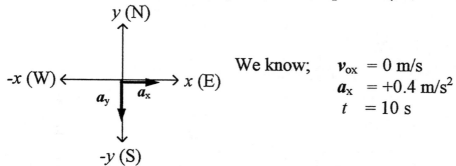

We know; $\quad v_{ox} = 0$ m/s
$a_x = +0.4$ m/s²
$t = 10$ s

We can find the final x-direction velocity by using;

$$v_x = v_{ox} + a_x\, t = (0 \text{ m/s}) + (+0.4 \text{ m/s}^2)(10 \text{ s}) = +4 \text{ m/s}$$

for the y-direction we know; $\quad v_{oy} = 0$ m/s
$a_y = -0.2$ m/s²
$t = 10$ s

and we can find the final y direction velocity the same way;

$$v_y = v_{oy} + a_y\, t = (0 \text{ m/s}) + (-0.2 \text{ m/s}^2)(10 \text{ s}) = -2 \text{ m/s}$$

We use the Pythagorean theorem to find the magnitude of the final velocity, *v*:

$$v = \sqrt{v_x^2 + v_y^2}$$

$$v = \sqrt{(4 \text{ m/s})^2 + (2 \text{ m/s})^2} = 4.5 \text{ m/s}$$

and finally, we find the direction using the inverse tangent function;

$$\theta = \tan^{-1}\left(\frac{v_y}{v_x}\right) = \tan^{-1}\left(\frac{2}{4}\right) = 27°$$

The final velocity of the ball is **4.5 m/s, 27° below the positive x-axis, or 27° south of east**.

9. *I throw a baseball in the air with an initial velocity of 11 m/s at an angle of 50° from the ground.*
(a) How long is it in the air before another person catches it (they catch it at the same level that it left my hand) ?

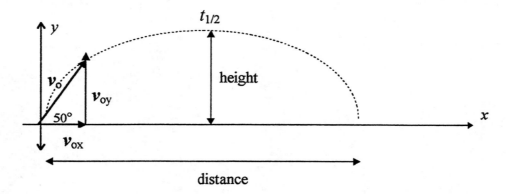

First we find v_{ox} and v_{oy} :

$$v_{ox} = (11 \text{ m/s}) \cos 50° = 7.1 \text{ m/s}$$

$$v_{oy} = (11 \text{ m/s}) \sin 50° = 8.4 \text{ m/s}$$

The time it's in the air is the time it takes to go up and down, or $2t_{1/2}$.

We can use the y-component to find the time it takes for the ball to get to the top of it's path ($t_{1/2}$), where $v_y = 0$ for an instant.

$$v_{oy} = +8.4 \text{ m/s}$$
$$a_y = -9.81 \text{ m/s}^2$$
$$v_y = 0 \text{ m/s}$$
$$t_{1/2} = ?$$

so $v_y = v_{oy} + a_y \, t_{1/2}$ can be rearranged to

$$t_{1/2} = \frac{v_y - v_{oy}}{a_y} = \frac{0 \text{ m/s} - 8.4 \text{ m/s}}{-9.81 \text{ m/s}^2} = 0.86 \text{ s}$$

So the total time is $2t_{1/2} = 2(0.86 \text{ s}) = $ **1.7 s.**

9.(b) How far does the ball go ?

> We use the x-component for this, since there's no acceleration in the x-direction, the velocity stays the same, so we can use $v = d/t$.

> so $\qquad v_{ox} = 7.1 \text{ m/s} = v_x$

> and $\qquad d = v_x t = (7.1 \text{ m/s})(1.7 \text{ s}) = \textbf{12.2 m}$

> I throw the ball a horizontal distance of 12.2 m

10. A plane drops a package from 1000 m above the ground. It's going +90 m/s when the package is released.
(a) What's the horizontal distance (d_x) the package travels before it hits the ground ?

> The package has the same horizontal velocity as the plane did when it was released.

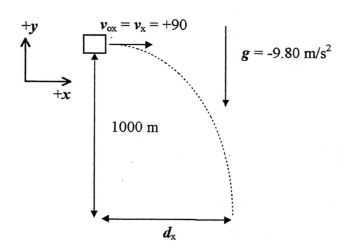

We know the velocity in the x-direction is constant, so we can use $v_x = d_x/t$ to find d_x. But first, we need to find t using the vertical (y) direction.

$$v_{oy} = 0 \text{ m/s}$$
$$a_y = -9.81 \text{ m/s}^2$$
$$d_y = -1000 \text{ m}$$
$$t = ?$$

Use $\qquad d_y = v_{oy} t + \dfrac{1}{2} a_y t^2 = \dfrac{1}{2} a_y t^2$, since $v_{oy} = 0 \text{ m/s}$.

so $\qquad t = \sqrt{\dfrac{2d_y}{a_y}} = \sqrt{\dfrac{2(\text{-}1000 \text{ m})}{(\text{-}9.81 \text{ m/s}^2)}} = \mathbf{14.3 \text{ s}}$

and so the horizontal distance is

$$d_x = v_x\, t = (+90 \text{ m/s})(14.3 \text{ s}) = \mathbf{1285 \text{ m}}$$

10. (b) What is the final velocity on impact ?

We know $v_x = +90$ m/s, so we need to find v_y on impact. We can use

$$v_y = v_{oy} + a_y\, t$$
$$= (0 \text{ m/s}) + (\text{-}9.81 \text{ m/s}^2)(14.3 \text{ s})$$
$$= \text{-}140 \text{ m/s}$$

We use the Pythagorean theorem to find the magnitude of the final velocity, v:

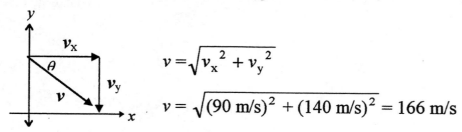

$$v = \sqrt{v_x{}^2 + v_y{}^2}$$

$$v = \sqrt{(90 \text{ m/s})^2 + (140 \text{ m/s})^2} = 166 \text{ m/s}$$

Find the direction using the inverse tangent function:

$$\theta = \tan^{-1}\!\left(\frac{v_y}{v_x}\right) = \tan^{-1}\!\left(\frac{140}{90}\right) = 57^\circ$$

Using some geometry, we'll find the angle above the ground:

remember that $90^\circ - 57^\circ = 33^\circ$.

The final velocity of the ball is **166 m/s, 33° above the ground.**

11. A plane is flying +900 km/hr west. A 30 km/hr wind, coming from the north-east kicks in. What speed and direction must the pilot change to in order to keep going +900 km/hr relative to the ground ?

We need to find out what kind of effect the wind will have on the plane.

We'll first find the velocity components of the wind, v_{wx} and v_{wy}.

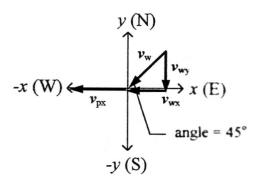

(The velocity vector of the plane isn't drawn to scale in the vector diagram). A north-east wind comes 45° above the +x-axis, or 45° right of the +y-axis.

First we find v_{wx} and v_{wy} :

$$v_{wx} = (30 \text{ km/hr}) \cos 45° = 21 \text{ km/hr, relative to the ground.}$$
$$v_{wy} = (30 \text{ km/hr}) \sin 45° = 21 \text{ km/hr, relative to the ground.}$$

The components are $v_{wx} = -21$ km/hr, and $v_{wy} = -21$ km/hr. We want to find the *new* x and y components of the plane's velocity, v_{px}' and v_{py}', such that these components, when added to the wind's x and y components, add up to a $v_p' = +900$ km/hr, west $= -900$ km/hr in the x-direction. We want:

$$v_{px}' + v_{wx} = -900 \text{ km/hr}$$
and
$$v_{py}' + v_{wy} = 0 \text{ km/hr}$$

so v_{px}' $= -900 \text{ km/hr} - v_{wx}$
$= -900 \text{ km/hr} - (-21 \text{ km/hr})$
$= -879 \text{ km/hr}$

and $v_{py}' = -v_{wy} = -(-21 \text{ km/hr}) = +21 \text{ km/hr}$

We use the Pythagorean theorem to find the magnitude of the new velocity of the plane, v_p'

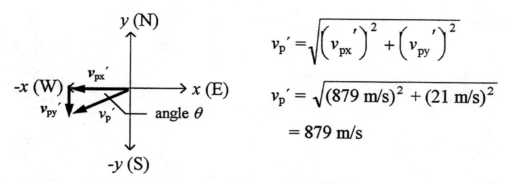

$$v_p' = \sqrt{\left(v_{px}'\right)^2 + \left(v_{py}'\right)^2}$$

$$v_p' = \sqrt{(879 \text{ m/s})^2 + (21 \text{ m/s})^2}$$

$$= 879 \text{ m/s}$$

Find the direction using the inverse tangent function:

$$\theta = \tan^{-1}\left(\frac{v_{py}'}{v_{px}'}\right) = \tan^{-1}\left(\frac{21}{879}\right) = 1.4°$$

The plane has to change its course to 879 km/hr, 1.4° south of west in the wind to continue going 900 km/hr west, relative to the ground.

Dynamics

The first part of this chapter was dealing with kinematics, now we're going to start to talk about *dynamics*. As I said before, dynamics deals with *forces*, and how they make things move. The big force guy was Isaac Newton. He wrote three laws of motion that we're going to talk about, but first, some definitions.

A **force** is usually a push or pull on an object, sometimes resulting in motion. Force is measured in Newtons (N).
Mass is how heavy something is. It's measured in kilograms (kg).
Weight is a force (measured in Newtons). Weight is equal to mass times acceleration due to gravity, *weight = mg*.

Newton's first law of motion: An object at rest stays at rest and an object in motion stays in motion, unless acted upon by a net force .
A **net force** is the vector sum of all forces acting on an object.

Newton's first law of motion basically says that an object will keep doing what ever it's doing if you don't mess with it. Think of a ball on a level table. When it's not moving, the only force acting on it is the force of gravity, which is balanced by the force of the table pushing on the ball; *the net force on the ball is zero when it's not accelerating.* If you now hit it with your finger then let it roll, you've given it a velocity, and it will roll for quite a while (usually until my cat sees it and wings it under the fridge, never to be seen again). The ball keeps rolling until some force acts on it, *creating a non-zero net force.* The force could be your finger, the wind, a wall, or my cat. In theory, if you never touched it, it would keep rolling forever. It doesn't roll forever due to the **force of friction** (and my cat). We talked about air resistance already. Well... the force of friction is like air resistance. It tries to stop objects in motion, so is *always* in the opposite direction of the acceleration..

All this net force stuff leads us to Newton's second law of motion;

Newton's second law of motion: When a net force acts on an object of mass m, an acceleration results which is related to the net force such that

$$F_{net} = ma.$$

The SI unit for force is: $(kg)(m/s^2)$ = Newton (N).

This also means that the direction of the force vector is the same as that of the acceleration vector. *Newton's second law means that the instant when you touch that ball on the table, you give the ball an acceleration which is directly related to how hard you touched it, and how heavy it is.*

Free Body Diagrams

Force problems in physics can be made much easier to solve if we draw a picture. This is even more important here than in kinematics, because we usually have more vectors to worry about. We use a diagram called a **free body diagram** to apply Newton's second law. In other words, a free body diagram includes the object the forces are acting on, and the vectors for all the forces acting on the object. This way we can easily find the net force which causes the motion. Time for an example !

Example: *Shawn and Jo are pushing Jase on a cart in the hallway. Shawn pushes with a force of 300 N, Jo pushes with a force of 335 N and there's a frictional force of 150 N opposing the acceleration because the wheels need to be oiled. The total mass of Jase and the cart is 80 kg. Find Jase's acceleration.*

First, we draw a free body diagram.

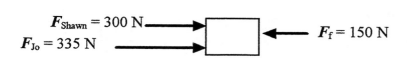

We add all the forces to find the net force;

$$F_{net} = F_{Shawn} + F_{Jo} + F_f$$
$$= +300 \text{ N} + (+335 \text{ N}) + (-150 \text{ N})$$
$$= +485 \text{ N}$$

Now that we know the net force, we can use it to find the acceleration using Newton's second law;

$$F_{net} = ma$$

$$a = \frac{F_{net}}{m} = \frac{+485 \text{ N}}{80 \text{ kg}} = 6.1 \text{ m/s}^2$$

(We can do some unit analysis to make sure we got the right units for acceleration. We had Newtons divided by kilograms in the equation;

$$\frac{N}{kg} = \frac{kg \cdot \frac{m}{s^2}}{kg} = \frac{kg \cdot m}{kg \cdot s^2} = \frac{m}{s^2}$$

m/s² are the correct units for acceleration.)

Jase's acceleration is +6.1 m/s² in the positive x direction.

Let's put that ball back on the table. When the ball is just sitting there, there is no net force since there is no acceleration. But we *know* that the force of gravity is acting on the ball, so what's happening ? The force of gravity on the ball is the force of the ball on the table top ($F_{b\,on\,t}$). Since there is no acceleration, then this force must be balanced, to make no *net* force. There has to be a *force the same size, but in the opposite direction* to balance the force of gravity. This is the force of the table on the ball ($F_{t\,on\,b}$). So

$$F_{b\,on\,t} = -F_{t\,on\,b}$$

(negative since it's in the opposite direction). This is Newton's third law.

Newton's third law of motion: When an object exerts a force on a second object, the second object exerts a force on the first of the same magnitude, but in the opposite direction.

In other words: every action has an equal, but opposite, reaction.

Newton's third law explains why both cars get wrecked if they collide, and why both you and your friend feel it if you bump into each other. When you walk on the ground, you exert a force on the ground, and the ground exerts a force on you.

Example: *Superhero-person has to stop a one million kilogram comet from hitting the Earth, and ending life on this planet as we know it. If the comet is traveling at 75 m/s, and it takes Superhero-person 30 seconds to bring the comet to a stop, what is the force Superhero-person applies to the comet ? What is the force the comet applies to Superhero-person ?*

We'll say that the comet was traveling in the positive x direction

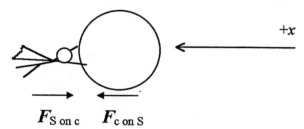

The initial velocity of the comet is +75 m/s, and the final velocity is 0 m/s, and we know the time. From this, we can find the acceleration of the comet.

Use

$$v = v_o + at$$

so

$$a = (v - v_o)/t$$
$$= (0 \text{ m/s} - 75 \text{ m/s})/30 \text{ s}$$
$$= -2.5 \text{ m/s}^2$$

Using Newton's second law, the force Superhero-person needs to apply to get this acceleration is

$$F_{S \text{ on } c} = ma$$
$$= (1 \times 10^6 \text{ kg})(-2.5 \text{ m/s})$$
$$= -2.5 \times 10^6 \text{ N}$$

from Newton's third law, we know that the force the comet applies to Superhero-person is equal in magnitude, but in the opposite direction of the force that Superhero-person applies to the comet, so

$$F_{c \text{ on } S} = 2.5 \times 10^6 \text{ N}$$

Example: *We have a 0.50 kg ball hanging on the end of a string. If you pull up on the string with a force of 15.0 N, what is the acceleration of the ball ?*

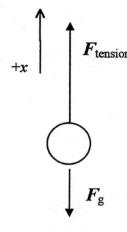

We'll define up as the positive x direction.

There are two forces acting on the ball: a force of tension ($F_{tension}$) from the string pulling the ball up (this is from you pulling on the string), and the force of gravity (F_g).

The $F_{tension}$ is just the force you're pulling with, so

$$F_{tension} = +15.0 \text{ N}$$

The force of gravity acting on the ball is in the negative x direction,

so
$$F_g = mg$$
$$= (0.50 \text{ kg})(-9.81 \text{ kg m/s}^2)$$
$$= -4.9 \text{ N}$$

The *net force* is

$$F_{net} = F_g + F_{tension}$$
$$= -4.9 \text{ N} + (+15.0 \text{ N})$$
$$= +10.1 \text{ N}$$

Since the net force is positive, we know the ball is being pulled *up*.

Now we can find the acceleration using Newton's second law.

$$F_{net} = ma$$

$$a = \frac{F_{net}}{m} = \frac{+10.1 \text{ N}}{0.50 \text{ kg}} = 20 \text{ m}/\text{s}^2$$

The ball accelerates upward at 20 m/s².

PHYSICS GRADE 11

The Normal Force

I think that it's best to start with the definition for the normal force:

> The **normal force** is the force a surface exerts on an object in contact with the surface. The direction of the normal force in always perpendicular to the surface.

In our example of the ball on the table, the normal force (F_N) is the force of the table on the ball (the word "normal" is sometimes used to mean "perpendicular"). Since the table is flat, the direction of the normal force is straight up.

$$F_N = +5 \text{ N}$$
$$F_g = -5 \text{ N}$$

For this example, the magnitude of the normal force is equal to the magnitude of the gravitational force (from Newton's third law). What if we pushed down on the ball with a force of 2 N ? What would the normal force be ?

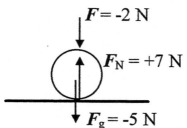

$$F = -2 \text{ N}$$
$$F_N = +7 \text{ N}$$
$$F_g = -5 \text{ N}$$

The total force trying to push the ball into the table is -2 N + (-5 N) = -7 N, so the normal force has to be +7 N. The table has to push on the ball with a normal force of +7 N for the ball to stay at rest (net force of zero). This makes sense, since we know from experience that if you push something straight down into a table, it doesn't go anywhere. If we attach

---

the a string to the ball, and pull straight up with a force of 2 N, the same rule applies; if the ball doesn't accelerate the net force is zero. So we have

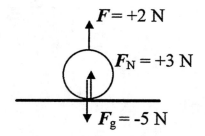

$$F = +2 \text{ N}$$
$$F_N = +3 \text{ N}$$
$$F_g = -5 \text{ N}$$

since (-5 N) + (+2 N) = +3 N. The upward force balances the downward force, so the ball stays at rest.

The next example involves an *inclined plane*. An inclined plane is a surface that is neither parallel, nor perpendicular to the Earth's surface. We'll have to use trig to solve the problem.

Example: *What is the normal force on a 5 kg box sitting on a hill, if the hill is 45° above the Earth's surface.*

For inclined plane problems, pictures are pretty much *necessary*.

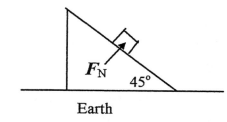

The normal force is perpendicular to the surface of the hill, as shown in the first diagram. We also know the force of gravity (*mg*) acts on the box, pulling it down towards the Earth, like in the second diagram.

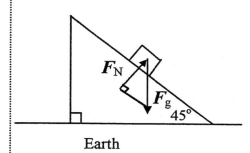

Now we have to remember some geometry. The big right-angle triangle and the little right-angle triangle are *similar triangles* (this means that the only difference between them is their sizes). This is easier to see if we flip and rotate the little triangle so that it's oriented the same way as the big one, like this:

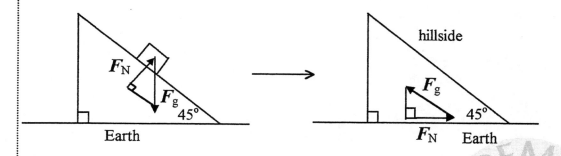

Since they are similar triangles, we know the angle between F_N and

---

F_g is the same as the angle between the Earth and the hillside, 45°. Now that we've got this figured out, we can go back and use trig to find the magnitude of the normal force.

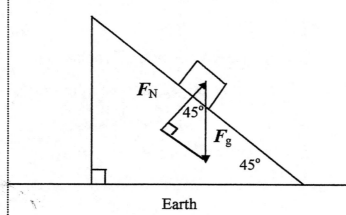

$$\cos 45° = \frac{\text{adj}}{\text{hyp}} = \frac{F_N}{F_g}$$

so $\qquad F_N = F_g \cos 45°$

but $\qquad F_g = mg$

so $\qquad F_N = mg \cos 45°$

$$F_N = mg \cos 45°$$
$$= (5.0 \text{ kg})(9.81 \text{ m/s}^2) \cos 45°$$
$$= 35 \text{ N}$$

The normal force is 35 N, perpendicular to the hillside, toward the box.

Friction

If you slide a box across a table, you feel a force resisting the motion that comes from the two surfaces rubbing together. This is if the force of **friction**. Frictional forces are always directed *parallel* to the surface.

Frictional force (F_f) exists when two objects are sliding across each other, like the box and table. It comes from the fact that the surfaces aren't perfectly smooth, and there are jagged bits from one surface hooking into the other surface. The rougher the surface, the more friction there is. This is why falling off your bike onto pavement roughs you up much more than falling onto a polished floor. The force of friction is **resistive**, which means it is always in the direction *opposite* to the direction of the motion.

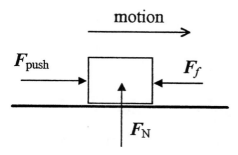

How big is this force ? It depends on the normal force. It makes sense that the heavier something is, the harder it is to drag it across the floor.

The frictional force has magnitude

$$F_f = \mu F_N$$

where μ is the **coefficient of friction** ("μ" is the Greek letter "mu"), and F_N is the magnitude of the normal force. The direction of the frictional force is *opposite* to the direction of motion.

The coefficient of friction, μ, is a proportionality constant which has no units, and depends on the roughness of the surfaces. A very smooth surface would have a very small coefficient of friction (like 0.005). The rougher the surface, the higher the coefficient. A high value for μ would be around 1.5.

Example: *Lee (50.0 kg) likes to slide on the polished school floors in his sock feet on rainy days. He takes a running start, getting to a speed of 7 m/s, before starting to slide. If the coefficient of friction is 0.100, and the wall is 20 m away from the point where he starts to slide, will he smack into the wall before he stops ?*

After Lee starts to slide, the only force acting on him (horizontally, anyway) is the force of friction between his socks and the floor. It's the force of friction which makes him decelerate, and eventually stop.

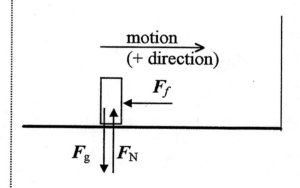

To find the frictional force, we need to know the size of the normal force. Since Lee doesn't move up or down, the vertical forces have to cancel out, so

$$F_N = F_g$$
$$F_N = mg$$
$$= (50.0 \text{ kg})(9.81 \text{ m/s}^2)$$
$$= 491 \text{ N}$$

So we can now use $\qquad F_f = \mu F_N$

$$= 0.100(491 \text{ N}) = 49.1 \text{ N}$$

The force of friction acting to decelerate Lee has a magnitude of 49.1 N, and is in the negative direction. We use Newton's second law to find the acceleration,

$$F_f = ma$$

$$a = \frac{F_f}{m} = \frac{-49.1 \text{ N}}{50.0 \text{ kg}} = -0.982 \text{ m} / \text{s}^2$$

The acceleration is in the negative direction.

Now that we know the acceleration, and since we know the initial and final velocities, we can use $v^2 = v_o^2 + 2ad$ to find out how far Lee could slide.

$$d = \frac{v^2 - v_o^2}{2a}$$

$$= \frac{(0 \text{ m/s})^2 - (7.0 \text{ m/s})^2}{2(-0.982 \text{ m/s}^2)}$$

$$= 25 \text{ m}$$

Lee *could* slide 25 m, which is further than the wall will let him. Smack!

The next example involves friction on an inclined plane.

Example: *Singh is pushing his sister up a hill in a cart. The angle of the surface of the hill to the Earth is 20°, and the coefficient of friction is 0.500. If Singh's sister and the cart have a total mass of 25.0 kg, how much force does he have to push with to accelerate the cart at 1.0 m/s² ?*

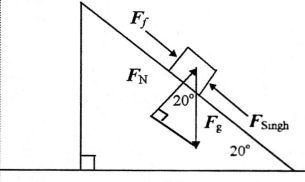

We can use Newton's second law to find what the net force up the hill has to be to get an acceleration of 1.0 m/s².

$$F_{net} = ma$$
$$= 25 \text{ kg } (1.0 \text{ m/s}^2)$$
$$= 25 \text{ N, up the hill}$$

So we know all the forces have to add up so that the total is 25 N up the hill. What are the other forces acting on the cart ? There's Singh's pushing (F_{singh}), the force of friction (F_f), and the component of the force of gravity acting on the cart that is parallel to the plane ($F_{g\,parallel}$), like this:

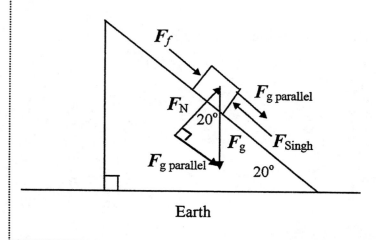

($F_{g\,parallel}$ is the other vector in the small triangle, since it's just the component of the F_g vector which is parallel to the hillside.)

---

we know that we have to have

$$\boldsymbol{F}_{net} = F_{singh} - F_f - F_{g\ parallel} = 25 \text{ N} \quad \text{(the negative signs are}$$

because gravity and frictional forces are *down* the hill)

so $\qquad F_{singh} = 25 \text{ N} + F_f + F_{g\ parallel}$ is what we want to find.

It's easy to find the other two forces, remember that the magnitude of

$\boldsymbol{F}_f$ is $\qquad\qquad\qquad F_f = \mu F_N$

and that $\qquad\qquad \cos 20° = \dfrac{adj}{hyp} = \dfrac{F_N}{F_g}$

so $\qquad\qquad F_N = F_g \cos 20°$

but $\qquad\qquad \boldsymbol{F}_g = m\boldsymbol{g}$

so $\qquad\qquad F_N = mg \cos 20°$

$$= 25.0 \text{ kg } (9.81 \text{ m/s}^2) \cos 20°$$

$$= 230 \text{ N}$$

so $\qquad\qquad F_f = \mu F_N = 0.500 \,(230 \text{ N}) = 115 \text{ N}$

and the force of gravity parallel to the hill is easy to find with trig.

$$\sin 20° = \dfrac{opp}{hyp} = \dfrac{F_{g\ parallel}}{F_g}$$

so $\qquad\qquad F_{g\ parallel} = F_g \sin 20°$

$$F_{g\ parallel} = mg \sin 20°$$

$$= 25.0 \text{ kg } (9.81 \text{ m/s}^2) \sin 20°$$

$$= 83.9 \text{ N}$$

We can now solve $F_{singh} = 25 \text{ N} + F_f + F_{g\ parallel}$

$$= 25 \text{ N} + 230 \text{ N} + 83.9 \text{ N} = 339 \text{ N}$$

To get the cart accelerating at a rate of 1 m/s², Singh has to push with

$F_{singh} = 339 \text{ N}$, up the hill.

Dynamics Practice Problems

1. A hockey player pushes a 200 g puck across the ice with a force of +5.0 N. Assuming there's no friction, what's the acceleration of the puck ?

2. A 1000 kg truck is accelerating at 2 m/s. Suddenly, an action movie hero falls into the back, making his heroic escape. If he weighs 100 kg, fully equipped, and the force applied by the truck is the same, what is the change in the acceleration ?

3. Four people are plying tug-a-rope. The two people on the left pull with 100 N and 89 N each, and the people on the right pull with 110 N and 60 N each. If the rope's mass is 1.0 kg, which side wins, and what is the acceleration ?

4. Perveen pulls a cart across the floor. She pulls on the handle with a force of 10 N, and the cart's handle is angled at 45° to the floor. If the cart's mass is 5 kg, what is the acceleration in the x-direction ?

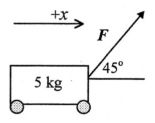

5. What is the normal force on each of the following 3.0 kg boxes ?

(a)

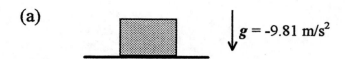

$g = -9.81$ m/s^2

(b)

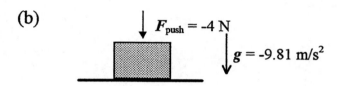

$F_{push} = -4$ N

$g = -9.81$ m/s^2

(c)

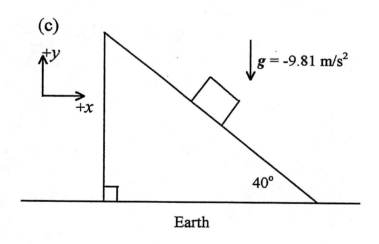

$g = -9.81$ m/s^2

$+y$

$+x$

$40°$

Earth

6. What is the acceleration of the 6.0 kg box, if the coefficient of friction, $\mu = 0.20$?

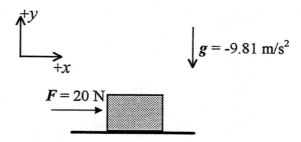

PHYSICS GRADE 11

7. Scott is trying to pull a box up a hill, as drawn below. The force of the pull is 100 N, the mass of the box is 10 kg, and the coefficient of friction is 0.50.

(a) What is the acceleration ?

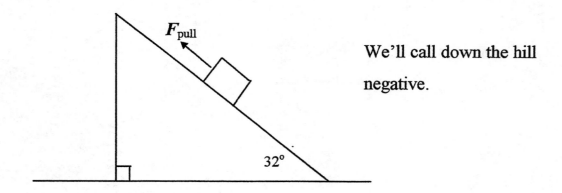

We'll call down the hill negative.

7. (b) What would F_{pull} have to be to hold the box at zero acceleration ?

8. The coefficient of friction between the plane and the box is 0.70. If there are no force other than the forces of gravity and friction acting on the box, what's the largest angle of the incline where the box won't slide ?

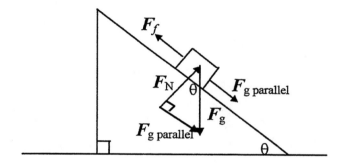

9. What force do we have to pull with to make the 0.25 kg ball accelerate at a rate of -3.0 m/s² ?

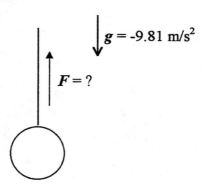

PHYSICS GRADE 11

Dynamics Practice Problem Solutions

*1. A hockey player pushes a 200 g puck across the ice with a force of
+5.0 N. Assuming there's no friction, what's the acceleration of the
puck ?*

Remember that 200 g = 0.200 kg.

We can find the acceleration using Newton's second law.

$$F_{net} = ma$$

$$a = \frac{F_{net}}{m} = \frac{5.0 \text{ N}}{0.200 \text{ kg}} = +25 \text{ m/s}^2$$

The ball accelerates across the ice at 25 m/s².

2. A 1000 kg truck is accelerating at 2 m/s. Suddenly, an action movie
hero falls into the back, making his heroic escape. If he weighs 100 kg,
fully equipped, and the force applied by the truck is the same, what is the
change in the acceleration ?

The force applied by the engine is

$$F_{net} = ma = (1000 \text{ kg})(+2 \text{ m/s}^2) = 2000 \text{ N}$$

This force is the same as the force after the hero boards. The

new mass is

$$m' = 1000 \text{ kg} + 100 \text{ kg} = 1100 \text{ kg}$$

and $\qquad F_{net} = m'a' = 2000 \text{ N}$

(the ′ symbol is for "after")

$$a' = \frac{F_{net}}{m'} = \frac{+2000 \text{ N}}{1100 \text{ kg}} = +1.82 \text{ m/s}^2$$

The trucks acceleration decreases to 1.82 m/s².

---

3. *Four people are plying tug-a-rope. The two people on the left pull with 100 N and 89 N each, and the people on the right pull with 110 N and 60 N each. If the rope's mass is 1.0 kg, which side wins, and what is the acceleration ?*

+x →

100 N ←

89 N ←

110 N →

60 N →

We'll find the net force:

$$F_{net} = 110\ N + 60\ N - 100\ N - 89\ N$$

$$= -19\ N$$

The net force is to the left, so **the left side wins.**

$$a = \frac{F_{net}}{m} = \frac{-19\ N}{1.0\ kg} = -19\ m/s^2$$

The acceleration is 19 m/s^2 to the left (since negative).

4. *Perveen pulls a cart across the floor. She pulls on the handle with a force of 10 N, and the cart's handle is angled at 45° to the floor. If the cart's mass is 5 kg, what is the acceleration in the x-direction ?*

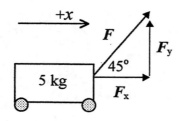

We break the force into x and y components, like in the diagram, and find the horizontal force, F_x.

$$F_x = F \cos 45° = (10\ N) \cos 45° = 7.1\ N$$

so $F_x = +7.1$ N, since in positive x-direction.

Now we can find the acceleration in the x-direction:

$$a = \frac{F_x}{m} = \frac{+7.1\ N}{5.0\ kg} = +1.4\ m/s^2$$

5. *What is the normal force on each of the following 3.0 kg boxes ?*

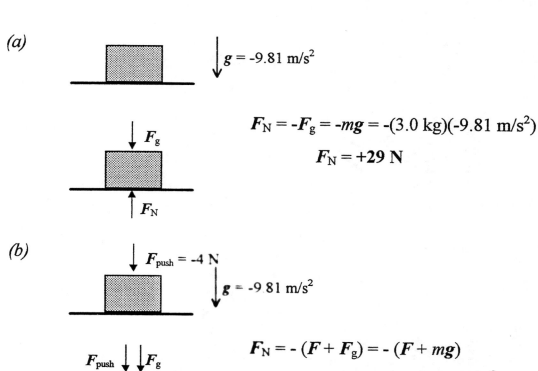

(a)

$$F_N = -F_g = -mg = -(3.0 \text{ kg})(-9.81 \text{ m/s}^2)$$
$$F_N = +29 \text{ N}$$

(b)

$$F_N = -(F + F_g) = -(F + mg)$$
$$= -[-4 \text{ N} + (3.0 \text{ kg})(-9.81 \text{ m/s}^2)]$$
$$F_N = +33 \text{ N}$$

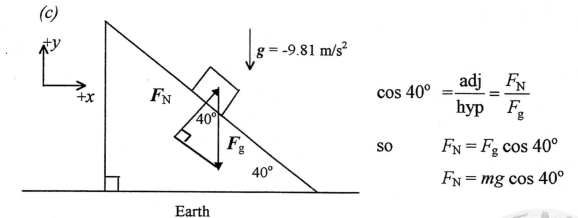

(c)

$$\cos 40° = \frac{\text{adj}}{\text{hyp}} = \frac{F_N}{F_g}$$

so $\quad F_N = F_g \cos 40°$

$$F_N = mg \cos 40°$$

$$F_N = mg \cos 40° = (3.0 \text{ kg})(9.81 \text{ m/s}^2) \cos 40° = 23 \text{ N}$$

so **$F_N = 23 \text{ N}$, 40° clockwise from the positive y-axis**.

6. What is the acceleration of the 6.0 kg box, if the coefficient of friction,
$\mu = 0.20$?

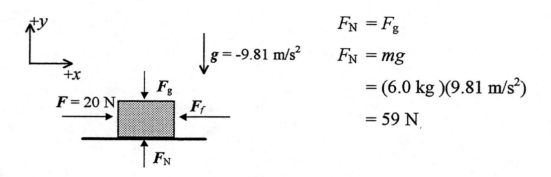

$$F_N = F_g$$

$$F_N = mg$$

$$= (6.0 \text{ kg})(9.81 \text{ m/s}^2)$$

$$= 59 \text{ N}$$

So we can now use

$$F_f = \mu F_N$$

$$= 0.20(59 \text{ N}) = 11.8 \text{ N}$$

(the direction is opposite the motion caused by *F*).

The net force in the x-direction is

$$F_{net} = 20 \text{ N} - 11.8 \text{ N} = +8.2 \text{ N}$$

so the acceleration is

$$a = \frac{F_{net}}{m} = \frac{+8.2 \text{ N}}{6.0 \text{ kg}} = +1.4 \text{ m/s}^2$$

7. *Scott is trying to pull a box up a hill, as drawn below. The force of the pull is 100 N, the mass of the box is 10 kg, and the coefficient of friction is 0.50.*
(a) What is the acceleration ?

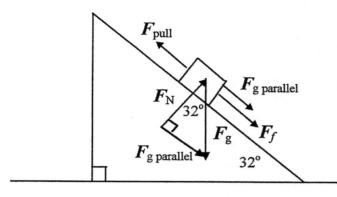

We'll call down the hill negative.

Find *magnitude of the normal force*: $F_N = F_g \cos 32°$

so $F_N = mg \cos 32°$

$$= 10 \text{ kg } (9.81 \text{ m/s}^2) \cos 32° = 83.2 \text{ N}$$

and the *force of gravity parallel to the hill*

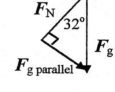

so $F_{g \text{ parallel}} = F_g \sin 32°$

$F_{g \text{ parallel}} = mg \sin 32°$

$$= 10 \text{ kg } (9.81 \text{ m/s}^2) \sin 32° = 52.0 \text{ N}$$

Now we can find *the frictional force*, $F_f = \mu F_N$

$$F_f = \mu F_N = 0.50 \ (83.2 \text{ N}) = 41.6 \text{ N}$$

Now, the *net force* is

$$F_{net} = F_{pull} - F_{g \text{ parallel}} - F_f$$

$$= 100 \text{ N} - 52.0 \text{ N} - 41.6 \text{ N} = +6.4 \text{ N}$$

And we can find the acceleration:

$$a = \frac{F_{net}}{m} = \frac{+6.4 \text{ N}}{10 \text{ kg}} = +0.64 \text{ m/s}^2$$

The box accelerates up the hill at 0.64 m/s².

7. (b) *What would F_{pull} have to be to hold the box at zero acceleration ?*

If $a = 0$, then $F_{net} = 0$, so

$$F_{net} = F_{pull} - F_{g\,parallel} - F_f = 0$$

so $\qquad F_{pull} = F_{g\,parallel} + F_f$

$$= 52.0\text{ N} + 41.6\text{ N} = 93.6\text{ N}$$

so $\qquad F_{pull} = \textbf{+93.6 N}$ (up the hill) for $a = 0\text{ m/s}^2$.

8. *The coefficient of friction between the plane and the box is 0.70. If there are no force other than the forces of gravity and friction acting on the box, what's the largest angle of the incline where the box won't slide ?*

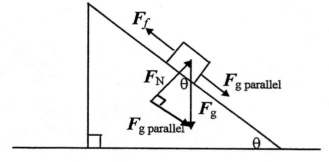

It won't side when

$$F_f = -F_{g\,parallel}$$

or when

$$F_f = F_{g\,parallel}$$

now $\qquad F_f = \mu F_N$ and $F_N = F_g \cos\theta$

so $\qquad F_f = \mu F_g \cos\theta$

Also, $\qquad F_{g\,parallel} = F_g \sin\theta$

so it won't slide when $\qquad \mu F_g \cos\theta = F_g \sin\theta$

or $\qquad \mu = \dfrac{\sin\theta}{\cos\theta}$

$$\mu = \tan\theta$$

Now, $\mu = 0.70$, so $\qquad 0.70 = \tan\theta$

$$\theta = \tan^{-1}(0.70) = 35° \quad \textbf{The largest angle is 35°.}$$

9. *What force do we have to pull with to make the 0.25 kg ball accelerate at a rate of -3.0 m/s² ?*

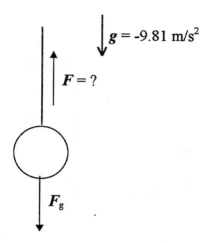

We know that $a = -3$ m/s², so we can find the net force:

$$F_{net} = ma = (0.25 \text{ kg})(-3.0 \text{ m/s}^2)$$

$$= -0.75 \text{ N}$$

The net force is the sum of the other forces acting on the ball:

$$F_{net} = F + F_g$$

so the force, F, we're looking for is equal to

$$F = F_{net} - F_g$$

Find the force of gravity acting on the ball:

$$F_g = mg = (0.25 \text{ kg})(-9.81 \text{ m/s}^2)$$

$$= -2.45 \text{ N}$$

so

$$F = F_{net} - F_g = -0.75 \text{ N} - (-2.45 \text{ N})$$

$$F = +1.70 \text{ N},$$

The force needed to accelerate the ball at -3 m/s² is +1.70 N (up).

PHYSICS GRADE 11

Work and Energy

Work

> When we talk about work, we usually think about doing something that takes energy, like shoveling the walk, or running somewhere. When we talk about work as physicists, we have a more specific definition.

Work: The work done on something by a constant force F by moving it through a distance d is

$$W = F \times d$$

Work is a scalar (it has no direction). The units for work are Joules (J).
$1\ J = 1\ N \cdot m$

This means that when we talk about work as *physicists*, we're talking about physically *moving* something. You could spend a day holding up a wall, but this wouldn't count as work as far as physics is concerned. You would have to move the wall somewhere else for it to count.

Example: *A Jules slides a 0.20 kg salt shaker 1.0 m across the table to his mom. He uses a force of 5.0 N the entire time. What is the work done by Jules in moving the salt ?*

We know that $W = F \times d$, so

$$W = (5.0\ N)(1.0\ m) = 5.0\ J$$

Jules uses 5.0 J of energy to slide the salt to his mom.

Kinetic Energy

When we do work, we usually expect to get something out of it. I know that I get pretty annoyed if I spend energy doing something, and I end up with the exact same thing that I started with. When we do work on an object by moving it, we change it by giving it a different velocity and kinetic energy (often called KE).

Kinetic Energy: The kinetic energy of something with a mass m, moving at a speed v is

$$KE = mv^2/2$$

Energy is a scalar quantity. The SI unit for energy is the Joule (J).

Kinetic energy depends on the mass of the object being moved, and how fast it's moving. Anything that is moving has a kinetic energy. By doing work on something, we change the object's kinetic energy. The change in the kinetic energy is equal to the work done on the object. This is called the work-energy theorem.

The work-energy theorem: If a net force does work (W) on something, it changes the kinetic energy of the object from some initial value (KE_i) to some final value (KE_f), and this difference in the kinetic energy is equal to the work done.

$$W = KE_f - KE_i = (mv_f^2)/2 - (m\, v_i^2)/2$$

Example: *A 65.0 kg snowboarder has a speed of 2.0 m/s at the start of her run. At the bottom of the hill, her speed is 15.0 m/s.*
(a) What is the kinetic energy at the beginning her run ? What is the kinetic energy at the end of her run ?

Since $\qquad KE = \frac{1}{2} mv^2,$

at the *beginning*:

$$KE_i = \frac{1}{2} m{v_i}^2 = \frac{1}{2} (65.0 \text{ kg})(2.0 \text{ m/s})^2 = \textbf{130 J}$$

at the *end*:

$$KE_f = \frac{1}{2} m{v_f}^2 = \frac{1}{2} (65.0 \text{ kg})(15.0 \text{ m/s})^2 = \textbf{7.31 x 10}^3 \textbf{ J}$$

(b) What was the work done in going down the hill ?

Since the work done is equal to the change in the kinetic energy (from the work-energy theorem),

$$W = KE_f - KE_i$$
$$= 7.31 \text{ x } 10^3 \text{ J} - 130 \text{ J}$$
$$= 7.31 \text{ x } 10^3 \text{ J} - 1.30 \text{ x } 10^2 \text{ J}$$

(this is 130 J in scientific notation)

$$= 7.31 \text{ x } 10^3 \text{ J} - 0.130 \text{ x } 10^3 \text{ J}$$

(the powers of ten have to be the same to add or subtract)

$$= \textbf{7.18 x 10}^3 \textbf{ J}$$

The work done was $7.18 \text{ x } 10^3$ J.

In this example, the snowboarder got *a lot* of energy from somewhere to increase her kinetic energy. Where did it come from ? It came from the force of gravity.

Gravitational Potential Energy

Gravity can do work on objects. You see this every time you drop a glass on the kitchen floor. It's the force of gravity that accelerates the glass toward the floor, and gives it a speed (and kinetic energy) before it smashes into little bits. We can measure work by looking at a change in gravitational potential energy, often called PE. Remember that $W = F \times d$, and the magnitude of the force of gravity on an object of mass m is mg. If something falls, we can say it started at some initial height (h_i), and stopped

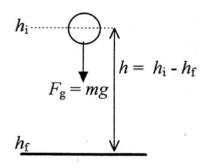

at some final height (h_f). This change in height can be called h. This is just the distance that the object moved. So, for an object accelerated by the force of gravity, the work done in falling is

$$W = F \times d$$
$$= mg \times (h_i - h_f)$$

or $$W = mg(h_i - h_f)$$

Any object raised above the ground has gravitational potential energy.

> **Gravitational potential energy**: Any object of mass m raised above the surface of the Earth has a gravitational potential energy
>
> $$PE = mgh,$$
>
> where h can be measured from any point above or at the surface of the Earth.
> The unit for energy is the Joule (J).

As an example, let's visit our snowboarder again.

Example: *The snowboarder (65.0 kg) does the exact same run as she did before, except this time, she doesn't know how fast she was going at the beginning and the end. She does know that she started 15.0 m above flat ground, and ended 2.75 m above flat ground. What was the work done in coming down the hill ?*

Since the only force making her move is the force of gravity, we can find the work done by looking at the change in gravitational potential energy.

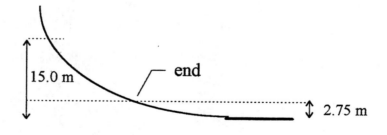

$$W = mg(h_i - h_f)$$
$$= (65.0 \text{ kg})(9.81 \text{ m/s}^2)(15.0 \text{ m} - 2.75 \text{ m})$$
$$= \mathbf{7.81 \times 10^3 \text{ J}}$$

Gravity does 7.81×10^3 J of work on the snowboarder. This is the same value for work that we found when we used the change in *kinetic* energy.

Conservation of Mechanical Energy

One of the things we believe as physicists is that energy can't be created or destroyed. It just moves around and changes. The chemical energy stored in a battery can be converted into electrical energy to run your CD player. In the same way, kinetic energy can be converted into potential energy (or heat, or sound), or potential energy can be converted into kinetic energy. Looking at the last two examples, we see that at the top of the hill, the snowboarder had a big potential energy, and a small kinetic energy. At the bottom of the hill, the opposite was true; she had a small potential energy and a big kinetic energy. Since the change in the kinetic energy in the first example and the change in the potential energy in the second example were the same, *the potential energy she lost going down the hill was converted into kinetic energy*. The sum of the kinetic energy and the potential energy at an instant in time is called the **total mechanical energy** (TE). It's important to keep in mind that we pretended there was no friction in these examples. Realistically, some energy would be lost because of friction, but we're going to ignore friction in this section.

The conservation of mechanical energy: The sum of kinetic energy and the gravitational potential energy is constant, if we ignore friction:

$$TE = KE + PE$$

Let's look at a 2 kg ball dropped from my hand 10 m above the ground. We can find the PE, KE and TE of the ball at any point in the fall using the principle of conservation of mechanical energy.

$h = 10$ m
$v = 0$ m/s

$PE = mgh = (2 \text{ kg})(9.81 \text{ m/s}^2)(10 \text{ m}) = 196 \text{ J}$

$KE = \frac{1}{2}mv^2 = 0 \text{ (since } v = 0)$

$TE = PE + KE = 196 \text{ J}$ this will *always* be the total energy of the ball during the fall.

$h = 3$ m

$PE = mgh = (2 \text{ kg})(9.81 \text{ m/s}^2)(3 \text{ m}) = 59 \text{ J}$

and $TE = PE + KE \ (= 196 \text{ J})$, so

$KE = TE - PE = 196 \text{ J} - 59 \text{ J} = 137 \text{ J}$

$h = 0$ m

$PE = 0 \text{ (since } h = 0)$

and $TE = PE + KE \ (= 196 \text{ J})$, so

$KE = TE - PE = 196 \text{ J} - 0 \text{ J} = 196 \text{ J}$

Before we release the ball, the total mechanical energy is all PE, since the speed is zero. Midway through the fall, the total mechanical energy is part KE and part PE. An instant before the ball touches the ground, the height is zero, so all the PE has been converted into KE. After the ball hits the floor, some energy is lost to the floor (it will shake a bit), and as noise. The ball will probably roll around a bit until friction eventually takes the rest of the energy.

Example: *I drop a glass from a height of three meters. From previous experience, I have found that this type of glass will break if it has a speed of 10 m/s when it hits something solid. Will I have to buy a new glass ?*

We can use the principle of conservation of mechanical energy to find the speed of the glass as it hits the floor. Before I drop the glass, it has a total energy = potential energy

$$PE_{before} = mgh$$

and just as it hits the floor, it has a total energy = kinetic energy

$$KE_{after} = \frac{1}{2}mv^2$$

Since total energy is constant,

$$PE_{before} = KE_{after}$$

so $\quad mgh = \frac{1}{2}mv^2$ (notice that we *don't* need to know the mass)

or $\quad v^2 = 2gh$

so $\quad v = \sqrt{2gh}$

$$= \sqrt{2(9.81 \text{ m/s}^2)(3.0 \text{ m})}$$

$$= 7.7 \text{ m/s}$$

The glass hits the floor with a speed of only 7.7 m/s (which is less than 10 m/s), so I don't have to buy a new glass.

You could also solve this problem using the kinematics equations, but I've always thought using the principle of the conservation of mechanical energy was much easier.

Example: *Lech is being chased by Zorgons. He sees a trench ahead of him as he is running, and leaps it. The far side of the trench is 1 m lower than the near side. If the trench is 3 m wide, what speed does he have when he hits the other side, if his initial (horizontal) speed is 5.0 m/s ?*

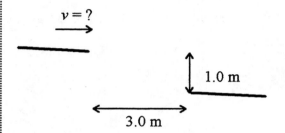

$v = ?$

1.0 m

3.0 m

We know that the initial total energy has the equal the final energy.

$$TE_i = TE_f$$

So $$KE_i + PE_i = KE_f + PE_f$$

We can say that the ground on the other side of the trench is at a height of zero, so $h_f = 0$, $h_i = 1.0$ m, and $PE_f = 0$.

so $$\frac{1}{2}mv_i^2 + mg\,h_i = \frac{1}{2}mv_f^2 \text{ (masses cancel again!)}$$

$$\frac{1}{2}v_i^2 + gh_i = \frac{1}{2}v_f^2$$

$$v_f^2 = v_i^2 + 2gh_i$$

$$v_f = \sqrt{v_i^2 + 2gh_i}$$

$$= \sqrt{(5.0 \text{ m/s})^2 + 2(9.81 \text{ m/s}^2)(1.0 \text{ m})}$$

$$= \sqrt{25.0 \text{ m}^2/\text{s}^2 + 19.6 \text{ m}^2/\text{s}^2}$$

$$= 6.7 \text{ m/s}$$

Lech will hit the other side with a speed of 6.7 m/s.

Power

Power is how we describe how *long it takes* to do an amount of work.

> **Power** is the rate of doing work:
>
> $$P = \text{work/time} = W/t$$
>
> The SI unit for power is the watt (W). 1 W = 1 J/s

Example: *A person pushes a stalled car 10 m with a force of 800 N for 2 minutes. He is then helped by a passerby for the next minute, so the combined force is 1700 N for the next 10 m. What are the two rates of power ?*

For the first 10 m, the work done is

$$W = F \times d = (800 \text{ N})(10 \text{ m}) = 8000 \text{ J}$$

$$\text{in } 2 \text{ min} = 2 \text{ min} \times 60 \text{ s/min} = 120 \text{ s.}$$

The power is

$$P = \frac{W}{t} = \frac{8000 \text{ J}}{120 \text{ s}} = \textbf{66.7 watts}$$

For the second 10 m, the work done is

$$W = F \times d = (1700 \text{ N})(10 \text{ m}) = 17000 \text{ J}$$

$$\text{in } 1 \text{ min} = 1 \text{ min} \times 60 \text{ s/min} = 60 \text{ s.}$$

The power is

$$P = \frac{W}{t} = \frac{17000 \text{ J}}{60 \text{ s}} = \textbf{283 watts}$$

PHYSICS GRADE 11

Work and Energy Practice Problems

1. (a) We push on a book with a force of 3.0 N, and move it a distance of 3.0 m. What is the work done (ignoring friction) ?

(b) If the book weighs 0.35 kg, how much work would be done to move it 2 m with an acceleration of 1.5 m/s^2 (ignoring friction) ?

(c) If in each of the two previous questions, the time it took to do the work was 10 seconds, what is the power in each case ?

PHYSICS GRADE 11

2. A 1000 kg truck has an initial velocity of 10 m/s. It accelerates until it has a velocity of 20 m/s . How much work was done by the engine ?

3. A 15 kg cart has an initial velocity of 1 m/s, and is pushed 12 m. If the force applied to push the cart is 12 N, what is the work done (ignoring friction).

4. What is the work done by a 65.0 kg skydiver falling 1100 m to the ground ? What is doing the work ?

5. A ball (initially at rest) falls from a height of 10 m above the ground, then is caught by someone when it's 2 m above the ground. What is its velocity the instant before it's caught ?

6. I throw a 100 g object into the air. It reaches a maximum height of 2.0 m above my hand, which is 1.1 m above the ground. What's the TE at the top of the path

(a) relative to my hand ?

(b) relative to the ground ?

7. I throw a baseball in the air with an initial speed of 5.0 m/s. It goes in an arc, then hits the ground at a point 2.0 m lower than I released it.
 (a) What maximum height does it reach ?

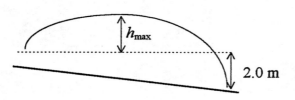

(b) What speed does it have when it hits the ground ?

8. We often talk about the horsepower of engines. One horsepower is 746 Watts (1 hp = 746 W). If a 800 kg car accelerates from rest at 5.0 m/s^2 for 10 m, what is the horsepower of the engine ?

Work and Energy Practice Problem Solutions

1. (a) We push on a book with a force of 3.0 N, and move it a distance of 3.0 m. What is the work done (ignoring friction) ?

A relation for work is:

$$W = F \times d$$

so

$$W = (3.0 \text{ N})(3.0 \text{ m}) = \textbf{9.0 J}$$

(b) If the book weighs 0.35 kg, how much work would be done to move it 2 m with an acceleration of 1.5 m/s^2 (ignoring friction) ?

The force we need to accelerate the book at 1.5 m/s^2 is

$$F_{net} = ma = (0.35 \text{ kg})(1.5 \text{ m/s}^2)$$

$$= 0.53 \text{ N}$$

so

$$W = F \times d$$

$$W = (0.53 \text{ N})(2.0 \text{ m}) = \textbf{1.1 J}$$

(c) If in each of the two previous questions, the time it took to do the work was 10 seconds, what is the power in each case ?

a)
$$P = \frac{W}{t} = \frac{9.0 \text{ J}}{10 \text{ s}} = \textbf{0.90 Watts}$$

a)
$$P = \frac{W}{t} = \frac{1.1 \text{ J}}{10 \text{ s}} = \textbf{0.11 Watts}$$

2. A 1000 kg truck has an initial velocity of 10 m/s. It accelerates until it has a velocity of 20 m/s. How much work was done by the engine ?

We can use the work-energy theorem:

$$W = KE_f - KE_i$$

So initially:

$$KE_i = \frac{1}{2} m v_i^2 = \frac{1}{2}(1000 \text{ kg})(10 \text{ m/s})^2 = 5.0 \times 10^4 \text{ J}$$

and finally:

$$KE_f = \frac{1}{2} m v_f^2 = \frac{1}{2}(1000 \text{ kg})(20 \text{ m/s})^2 = 2.0 \times 10^5 \text{ J}$$

So

$$W = KE_f - KE_i$$
$$= 2.0 \times 10^5 \text{ J} - 5.0 \times 10^4 \text{ J}$$
$$= 2.0 \times 10^5 \text{ J} - 0.50 \times 10^5 \text{ J}$$
$$\mathbf{W = 1.5 \times 10^5 \text{ J}}$$

3. A 15 kg cart has an initial velocity of 1 m/s, and is pushed 12 m. If the force applied to push the cart is 12 N, what is the work done (ignoring friction).

It doesn't matter that the cart isn't initially at rest, we can use

$$W = F \times d$$
$$W = (12 \text{ N})(12 \text{ m}) = \mathbf{144 \text{ J}}$$

We could find the final velocity, and take the difference in the kinetic energies using the work-energy theorem and get the same answer, but it's much longer to do it that way.

4. What is the work done by a 65.0 kg skydiver falling 1100 m to the ground ? What is doing the work ?

$$W = mg(h_i - h_f)$$
$$= (65.0 \text{ kg})(9.81 \text{ m/s}^2)(1100 \text{ m} - 0 \text{ m})$$
$$= \mathbf{7.0 \times 10^5 \text{ J}}$$

The force of gravity is doing the work.

5. A ball (initially at rest) falls from a height of 10 m above the ground, then is caught by someone when it's 2 m above the ground. What is its velocity the instant before it's caught ?

We can use the conservation of mechanical energy to solve this:

$$TE = KE + PE = \text{constant}$$

The initial total energy, relative to the person's hand is

$$TE_i = KE_i + PE_i,$$

The initial velocity is zero, so the KE_i is zero, and so

$$TE_i = PE_i.$$

As the ball strikes the hand, all the PE has been transformed into KE, so

$$TE_f = KE_f.$$

So now,
$$TE_i = TE_f$$
$$PE_i = KE_f$$
$$mgh = \frac{1}{2}mv_f^2$$
$$v_f^2 = 2gh$$

The ball falls a total of 10 m - 2 m = 8 m to the person's hand.

so
$$v_f = \sqrt{2gh} = \sqrt{2(9.81 \text{ m/s}^2)(8.0 \text{ m})}$$

$$v_f = \mathbf{12.5 \text{ m/s}}$$

The final velocity is -12.5 m/s, since the ball is falling down.

---

6. *I throw a 100 g object into the air. It reaches a maximum height of 2.0 m above my hand, which is 1.1 m above the ground. What's the TE at the top of the path*
(a) relative to my hand ?

Remember that 100 g = 0.100 kg

At the maximum height, $v = o$, so

$$TE = PE = mgh$$

$$= (0.100 \text{ kg})(9.81 \text{ m/s}^2)(2.0 \text{ m})$$

$$= \textbf{2.0 J}$$

(b) relative to the ground ?

h is now 2.0 m + 1.1 m = 3.1 m

so $\qquad TE = PE = mgh$

$$= (0.100 \text{ kg})(9.81 \text{ m/s}^2)(3.1 \text{ m})$$

$$= \textbf{3.0 J}$$

PHYSICS GRADE 11

7. *I throw a baseball in the air with an initial speed of 5.0 m/s. It goes in an arc, then hits the ground at a point 2.0 m lower than I released it.*
(a) What maximum height does it reach ?

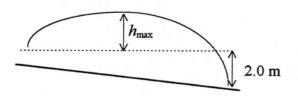

As the objects leaves my hand , all the energy is kinetic. At the top of the path (at h_{max}), all the energy is potential energy, since $v = 0$ at the top. So $\qquad KE_i = PE_{top}$

$$\frac{1}{2}mv_i{}^2 = mgh_{max}$$

$$h_{max} = \frac{v_i{}^2}{2g} = \frac{(5.0 \text{ m/s})^2}{2(9.81 \text{ m/s}^2)} = \textbf{1.3 m, relative to}$$

my hand.

(b) What speed does it have when it hits the ground ?

The ball falls another 2 m past the level of my hand, so it falls 2.0 m + 1.3 m = 3.3 m to the ground. All the this PE in converted into KE just before it hit the ground, so

$$KE_f = PE_{top \text{ (rel. to the ground)}}$$

$$\frac{1}{2}mv_i{}^2 = mgh$$

$$v_f{}^2 = 2gh$$

so $\qquad v_f = \sqrt{2gh} = \sqrt{2(9.81 \text{ m/s}^2)(3.3 \text{ m})}$

$$v_f = \textbf{8.0 m/s}$$

The final velocity is -8.0 m/s, since the object is falling down.

8. *We often talk about the horsepower of engines. One horsepower is 746 Watts (1 hp = 746 W). If a 800 kg car accelerates from rest at 5.0 m/s² for 10 m, what is the horsepower of the engine ?*

To find the work done, we need to find the force

$$F = ma = (800 \text{ kg})(5.0 \text{ m/s}^2) = 4000 \text{ N}$$

so

$$W = F \times d = 4000 \text{ N} \times 10 \text{ m} = 4.0 \times 10^4 \text{ W}$$

is the work done.

How long does this take ?

$$d = v_o\, t + \frac{1}{2} a t^2 = \frac{1}{2} a t^2 \text{ (since } v_o = 0\text{)}$$

or

$$d = \frac{1}{2} a t^2$$

so

$$t = \sqrt{\frac{2d}{a}} = \sqrt{\frac{2(10 \text{ m})}{5.0 \text{ m/s}^2}} = 2.0 \text{ s}$$

Now we can find the power:

$$P = \frac{W}{t} = \frac{4.0 \times 10^4 \text{ J}}{2.0 \text{ s}} = 2.0 \times 10^4 \text{ Watts}$$

In horsepower, this is

$$P = 2.0 \times 10^4 \text{ W} \times \frac{1 \text{ hp}}{746 \text{ W}} = \textbf{28 hp}$$

PHYSICS GRADE 11

Uniform Circular Motion

In the last sections, we've used Newton's laws to talk about things moving in straight lines in one or two dimensions. We can also use these laws to talk about things moving at a constant speed in two dimensional circles: **uniform circular motion**. We see this type of motion all the time: midway rides, figure skaters, cars on circular roads.

> **Uniform circular motion** is happening when something is moving at a constant (uniform) speed on a circular path.

If we have a ball twirled on a string, the *speed* at all points on the path is the same, but the *velocity* is different at each point. The velocity is different because the ball's direction of travel is always changing.

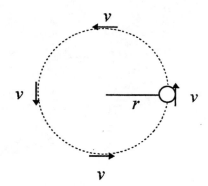

How can we find the speed of the ball ? Remember how we found the speed in linear motion. We used

$$v = \frac{\Delta d}{\Delta t}$$

We'll use the time it takes to go around the circle once (T = 1 **period**). The distance the ball goes in this time is equal to the circumference of the circle, $C = 2\pi r$, where r is the radius of the circle. So

$$v = \frac{\Delta d}{\Delta t} = \frac{2\pi r}{T}$$

The speed of the ball depends on the radius of the circle, and the period (time).

Sometimes we talk about the **frequency** of objects in uniform circular motion. Frequency (*f*) is defined as

$$f = \frac{1}{T}, \quad \text{where T is the period.}$$

The frequency is the number of revolutions (complete circles) per second. The unit for frequency is 1/s, called **Hertz** (Hz).

A **period** (T) is the time in seconds it takes for an object to complete one revolution (one complete circle).

The **speed** of an object in uniform circular motion is $v = (2\pi r)/T$.

Frequency (*f*) is the number of revolutions per second, $f = 1/T$, measured in Hertz (Hz).

Example: *A rock twirled overhead on a string takes 2 seconds for each circle. The radius of the circle is 30 cm.*
(a) How fast is the rock circling ?

It takes 2 s for each circle, so the period is 2 s.

Remember that 30 cm = 0.30 m.

$$v = \frac{2\pi r}{T} = \frac{2\pi(0.30 \text{ m})}{2 \text{ s}} = \textbf{0.94 m/s}$$

(b) What is its frequency ?

The period is 2 s, so

$$f = \frac{1}{T} = \frac{1}{2 \text{ s}} = \textbf{0.5 Hz}$$

Uniform Circular Motion

Centripetal Acceleration

We just talked about how the speed is constant in uniform circular motion, but the velocity is not. When we learned about kinematics, we learned that an object which is changing its velocity is accelerating. In the case of uniform circular motion, there's a special kind of acceleration, called **centripetal acceleration**. "Centripetal" means "centre-seeking". It's called centripetal acceleration, because the direction is always toward the centre of the circle. We can use Newton's first law to show this (Newton's first law is the "objects in motion stay in motion, and objects at rest stay at rest unless acted upon by a net force" law). Look at this picture.

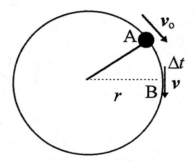

At point A, the velocity vector, v_o, is in the direction shown. The object has a *different* velocity v at B, at some later time (remember, only the direction has changed, *not* the speed).

According the Newton's first law, the velocity (in this case, only the direction) can only change if the is a net force acting on the object. And according the Newton's second law ($F = ma$), if there's a net force, there *has* to be an acceleration. What about the direction ? Look at the next picture.

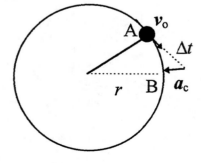

If there was no net force (no acceleration), the object would follow the dotted path. The only way the object *gets* to B is if the acceleration is directed toward the centre of the circle. The magnitude of the centripetal acceleration, a_c, is

$$a_c = \frac{v^2}{r}.$$

> **Centripetal acceleration**: The magnitude of the centripetal acceleration for uniform circular motion is
>
> $$a_c = v^2/r,$$
>
> where v is the speed, and r is the radius of the circular path. The centripetal acceleration is always directed toward the centre of the circle.

Centripetal Force

As I just mentioned, since there's an acceleration, there's a force. The net force is in the same direction as the acceleration, we have a **centripetal force** (F_c). We can find the magnitude of the centripetal force with Newton's second law and the definition for centripetal acceleration:

$$F_c = ma_c = m\,\frac{v^2}{r} = \frac{mv^2}{r}$$

> **Centripetal force**: A centripetal force acts on any object in uniform circular motion. The force has a magnitude
>
> $$F_c = mv^2/r,$$
>
> where m is the mass of the object, v is the speed, and r is the radius of the circle. F_c is always directed toward the centre of the circle.

Example: *(a) A 90 kg bicyclist travels at 5.0 m/s around a curve of radius 12 m. What is the centripetal acceleration and centripetal force ?*

The magnitude of the centripetal acceleration is

$$a_c = \frac{v^2}{r} = \frac{(5.0 \text{ m/s})^2}{12 \text{ m}} = 2.1 \text{ m/s}^2$$

so **$a_c = 2.1$ m/s^2 toward the centre of the circle.**

The magnitude of the centripetal force is

$$F_c = m \frac{v^2}{r} = \frac{(90 \text{ kg})(5.0 \text{ m/s})^2}{12 \text{ m}} = 189 \text{ N}$$

so **$F_c = 189$ N toward the centre of the circle.**

(b) What is the centripetal acceleration and centripetal force if the curve radius is 5.0 m ?

The magnitude of the centripetal acceleration is

$$a_c = \frac{v^2}{r} = \frac{(5.0 \text{ m/s})^2}{5.0 \text{ m}} = 5.0 \text{ m/s}^2$$

so **$a_c = 5.0$ m/s^2 toward the centre of the circle.**

The magnitude of the centripetal force is

$$F_c = m \frac{v^2}{r} = \frac{(90 \text{ kg})(5.0 \text{ m/s})^2}{5.0 \text{ m}} = 450 \text{ N}$$

so **$F_c = 450$ N toward the centre of the circle.**

We see here that there rider feels a stronger force going a round a tighter curve. This is why we have to slow down before going around a curve, like a highway exit ramp.

You might ask, "Christine, what is causing this centripetal force ?" "That depends." I would answer. If the object we're talking about is a rock on a string, the tension of the string supplies the force. For a bicycle or car going around a turn, the friction of the wheels on the pavement supplies the force. This is why you have to more slowly when the roads are slippery; there's a lower coefficient of friction, so the frictional force is smaller. The planets circling the Sun, or a satellite circling the Earth are examples of uniform circular motion. Here the centripetal force is the gravitational attraction. The electrons in an atom circle the positive nucleus because of electrical attraction. In an atom, the centripetal force is an electric force.

Example: *Kim is traveling in his car in slippery highway conditions. He sees a curve in the road ahead, and quickly throws his physics 20 notes to his passenger, and tells him to calculate the maximum speed they can take the curve. They assume the radius of the curve is 50.0 m, and the coefficient of friction is 0.100.*

The centripetal force is caused by the friction between the wheels and the road. We need to find what the maximum force of friction (F_f) is first. We said that the maximum force of friction is

$$F_f = \mu F_N$$

(remember that μ = the coefficient of static friction, and F_N = the normal force). The normal force is caused by the force of gravity acting on the car, so

$$F_N = mg$$

so the maximum force of friction is

$$F_f = \mu F_N = \mu mg$$

but the centripetal force is caused by the force of friction, so

$$F_c = F_f$$

and $$F_c = m\,\frac{v^2}{r}$$

so $$F_f = \mu mg = m\,\frac{v^2}{r}$$

then the maximum velocity Kim can drive around the curve is

$$v^2 = \mu gr \quad \text{(so we don't need to know the mass!)}$$

or $$v = \sqrt{\mu gr}$$

$$= \sqrt{0.100(9.81 \text{ m/s}^2)(50.0 \text{ m})}$$

$$= 7.00 \text{ m/s}$$

What is this in km/hr ?

$$7.00\ \frac{\text{m}}{\text{s}} \times \frac{1}{1000}\ \frac{\text{km}}{\text{m}} \times 3600\ \frac{\text{s}}{\text{hr}} = 25.2 \text{ km/hr}$$

Kim can go a maximum of 25.2 km/hr around the turn safely.

You can see the problem with curves on highways: the maximum speed the car can go depends a lot on the road conditions. Sometimes designers using **road banking** to help eliminate the importance of friction. Banked curves are at an angle, like this:

unbanked: F_N
is straight up.

banked: F_N is
at an *angle*.

The car that is going around the banked curve has one component of its normal force going straight up, and one component of its normal force going toward the centre of the circular path (centripetal*). On a banked curve, part of the normal force is a centripetal force.* This means that friction doesn't have to be all the centripetal force. In fact, we can go around banked curves even if there is no friction at all! If we tried to do this on the flat highway, we would end up in the ditch. Let's look at the forces acting on the car going around the banked curve (ignoring friction). I've split the normal force into its straight up and centripetal components using trig.

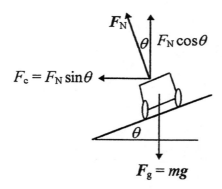

We'll assume that the car doesn't go flying into the air, so the magnitudes of the up and down components are equal, so

$$F_N \cos \theta = F_g = mg$$

and the centripetal component of the normal force is

$$F_c = F_N \sin \theta$$

but remember that
$$F_c = \frac{mv^2}{r}, \text{ so}$$

$$\frac{mv^2}{r} = F_N \sin\theta$$

we can divide $F_N \sin\theta$ by $F_N \cos\theta$,

$$\frac{F_N \sin\theta}{F_N \cos\theta} = \frac{\dfrac{mv^2}{r}}{mg}$$

$$\frac{\sin\theta}{\cos\theta} = \frac{v^2}{rg}$$

but $\tan\theta = \dfrac{\sin\theta}{\cos\theta}$, so we have this relation for banked curves

$$\tan\theta = \frac{v^2}{rg}.$$

Example: *A highway designer wants to build a banked curve that cars can travel around at 80 km/hr. If the radius of the curve has to be 100 m, what angle should the bank have ?*

We can use the relation we just derived, but first, we have to convert 80 km/hr in to m/s:

80 km/hr = 80 ~~km/hr~~ x 1000 m/~~km~~ x 1/60 ~~hr/min~~ x 1/60 ~~min~~/s

$$= 22 \text{ m/s}$$

$$\tan\theta = \frac{v^2}{rg} = \frac{(22 \text{ m/s})^2}{100 \text{ m} (9.81 \text{ m/s}^2)}$$

$$= 0.49$$

so $\qquad \theta = \tan^{-1}(0.49) = 26°$

The angle the designer wants is 26°.

Uniform Vertical Circular Motion

So far we've only talked about circular motion in a plane parallel to the Earth's surface. We can use the same ideas to talk about the circular motion that is in a plane perpendicular to the surface of the Earth, like a stunt loop-the-loop. Take a look at the next diagram, which represents a car driving around a loop-the-loop. We can look at the forces cause by the weight of the car, and the normal force of the loop pushing on the car (ignoring friction). Remember that the centripetal force isn't some special force, it is just the net force directed toward the centre of the circle. you can see from the picture that the normal force is always centripetal, and at the top of the loop, the force of gravity is centripetal. We get write down four simple equations for the uniform vertical circular motion (remember that $F_c = \dfrac{mv^2}{r}$).

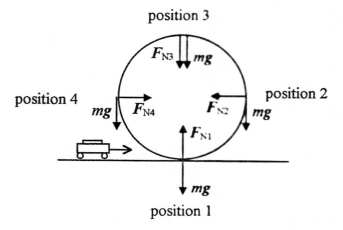

$$\text{position 1:} \quad F_c = \frac{mv^2}{r} = F_{N1} - mg$$

$$\text{position 2:} \quad F_c = \frac{mv^2}{r} = F_{N2}$$

$$\text{position 3:} \quad F_c = \frac{mv^2}{r} = F_{N3} + mg$$

$$\text{position 4:} \quad F_c = \frac{mv^2}{r} = F_{N4}$$

PHYSICS GRADE 11

We can use any of these equations to solve vertical circular motion problems.

Example: *What is the minimum speed a roller coaster car train needs to have to make a 40 m diameter loop-the-loop ?*

Notice that we don't know the mass. Let's look at the forces on the cars at the top of the loop. We know that at the top of the loop, both the

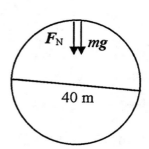

normal force and the force of gravity are centripetal, so

$$F_c = \frac{mv^2}{r} = F_N + mg$$

At the *minimum* speed, the cars would not push against the track, so the track would not push against the cars (no normal force!). All the centripetal force would be from the force of gravity, so

$$F_c = \frac{mv^2}{r} = 0 + mg$$

$$\frac{mv^2}{r} = mg, \qquad \text{the mass cancels out, so}$$

$$\frac{v^2}{r} = g, \qquad \text{so we can rearrange to solve for } v.$$

$$v^2 = gr$$

remember that the *diameter* is 40 m, so the *radius* is 40m/2 = 20 m.

$$v = \sqrt{gr} = \sqrt{(9.81 \text{ m/s}^2)(20 \text{ m})}$$
$$= 14 \text{ m/s}$$

The minimum speed needed is 14 m/s.

PHYSICS GRADE 11

Uniform Circular Motion Practice Problems

1. Joe Western Guy twirls his lasso over his head to catch a runaway steer. If the circle has a diameter of 1.5 m, and it takes 0.80 s to complete one circle

(a) How fast is the loop twirling ?

(b) What is its frequency ?

(c) What is the centripetal acceleration ?

(d) What is the centripetal force if the mass of the loop is 0.50 kg ? What causes the centripetal force ?

---

2. (a) A potter sticks a bit of clay (mass = 0.020 kg) 3.0 cm from the centre of the potting wheel. If the period of the wheel is 0.25 s, what is the magnitude of the centripetal force the bit of clay experiences ?

(b) If the clay is 15 cm from the centre of the wheel, what's F_c ?

(c) Based on these two calculations, why does the potter have to slow the wheel down when working on pieces with a large diameter ?

3. A car goes around an unbanked curve of radius 100 m at 20 m/s without slipping. What's the smallest possible coefficient of friction between the tires and the pavement ?

4. A biker goes around a banked curve of diameter 13 m. The angle of the bank is 7°. How fast can the biker go in lousy weather, when there's no friction between the road and the wheels (in km/hr) ?

5. A plane does a loop-the-loop. At the top of the loop, everyone feels weightless for an instant. If the speed of the plane is 220 m/s, what is the radius of the loop ?

6. A 75 kg cyclist goes through a circular dip in the path of radius 5.0 m, at 6.0 m/s. What is the normal force ?

Uniform Circular Motion Practice Problem Solutions

1. Joe Western Guy twirls his lasso over his head to catch a runaway steer. If the circle has a diameter of 1.5 m, and it takes 0.80 s to complete one circle
(a) How fast is the loop twirling ?

It takes 0.80 s for each circle, so the period is 0.80 s.

$$r = \text{diameter}/2 = 1.5/2 \text{ m} = 0.75 \text{ m}$$

$$v = \frac{2\pi r}{T} = \frac{2\pi(0.75 \text{ m})}{0.80 \text{ s}} = \textbf{5.9 m/s}$$

(b) What is its frequency ?

The period is 0.80 s, so

$$f = \frac{1}{T} = \frac{1}{0.80 \text{ s}} = \textbf{1.25 Hz}$$

(c) What is the centripetal acceleration ?

$$a_c = \frac{v^2}{r} = \frac{(5.9 \text{ m/s})^2}{0.75 \text{ m}} = 46 \text{ m/s}^2$$

so $\qquad a_c = \textbf{46 m/s}^2$ **toward the centre of the circle.**

(d) What is the centripetal force if the mass of the loop is 0.50 kg ? What causes the centripetal force ?

$$F_c = m \frac{v^2}{r} = \frac{(0.50 \text{ kg})(5.9 \text{ m/s})^2}{0.75 \text{ m}} = 23 \text{ N}$$

so $\qquad F_c = \textbf{23 N toward the centre of the circle.}$

The force is caused by the tension in the rope.

2. (a) *A potter sticks a bit of clay (mass = 0.020 kg) 3.0 cm from the centre of the potting wheel. If the period of the wheel is 0.25 s, what is the magnitude of the centripetal force the bit of clay experiences ?*

Remember that 3.0 cm = 0.030 m

and
$$F_c = m\,\frac{v^2}{r} = \frac{m}{r}\left(\frac{2\pi r}{T}\right)^2$$

since
$$v = \frac{2\pi r}{T}.$$

$$F_c = \frac{4\pi^2 mr}{T^2} = \frac{4\pi^2(0.020\text{ kg})(0.030\text{ m})}{(0.25\text{ s})^2} = \mathbf{0.38\ N}$$

(b) *If the clay is 15 cm from the centre of the wheel, what's F_c ?*

$$F_c = \frac{4\pi^2 mr}{T^2} = \frac{4\pi^2(0.020\text{ kg})(0.15\text{ m})}{(0.25\text{ s})^2} = \mathbf{1.9\ N}$$

(c) *Based on these two calculations, why does the potter have to slow the wheel down when working on pieces with a large diameter ?*

As the radius increases, the centripetal force on the clay gets bigger. This could result in the clay spinning off the wheel.

If we slow the wheel down, we increase the time it takes to complete one revolution (the period, T). If we increase T as r increases, we can keep a constant centripetal force (we found above that

$F_c = \dfrac{4\pi^2 mr}{T^2}$), and keep the clay in place.

3. A car goes around an unbanked curve of radius 100 m at 20 m/s without slipping. What's the smallest possible coefficient of friction between the tires and the pavement ?

The maximum force of friction is

$$F_f = \mu F_N$$

The normal force is caused by the force of gravity acting on the car, so

$$F_N = F_g = mg$$

so the maximum force of friction is

$$F_f = \mu F_N = \mu mg .$$

and $$F_c = m \frac{v^2}{r}$$

The centripetal force is caused by the force of friction, so

$$F_c = F_f$$

so $$m\frac{v^2}{r} = \mu mg$$

$$\mu = \frac{v^2}{rg} = \frac{(20 \text{ m/s})^2}{(100 \text{ m})(9.81 \text{ m/s}^2)} = \textbf{0.41}$$

4. A biker goes around a banked curve of diameter 13 m. The angle of the bank is 7°. How fast can the biker go in lousy weather, when there's no friction between the road and the wheels (in km/hr) ?

$$\tan\theta = \frac{v^2}{rg}$$

so $$v^2 = rg \tan\theta$$

$r = $ diameter/2 $= (13 \text{ m})/2 = 6.5 \text{ m}$

$$v = \sqrt{rg \tan\theta} = \sqrt{(6.5 \text{ m})(9.81 \text{ m/s}^2) \tan 7°} = 2.8 \text{ m/s}$$

in km/hr: $$2.8 \frac{m}{s} \times \frac{1}{1000} \frac{km}{m} \times 3600 \frac{s}{hr} = 10 \text{ km/hr}$$

The maximum speed is 10 m/s.

5. *A plane does a loop-the-loop. At the top of the loop, everyone feels weightless for an instant. If the speed of the plane is 220 m/s, what is the radius of the loop ?*

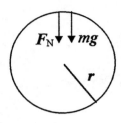

F_N and F_g are both centripetal at the top. The fact that the passengers feel weightless for an instant means that the normal force is zero at the top.

$$F_c = \frac{mv^2}{r} = F_N + mg$$

$$F_c = \frac{mv^2}{r} = 0 + mg$$

so

$$\frac{mv^2}{r} = mg,$$

and then

$$r = \frac{v^2}{g} = \frac{(220 \text{ m/s})^2}{9.81 \text{ m/s}^2} = \textbf{4.93} \times \textbf{10}^3 \textbf{ m}$$

6. *A 75 kg cyclist goes through a circular dip in the path of radius 5.0 m, at 6.0 m/s. What is the normal force ?*

$$F_c = \frac{mv^2}{r} = F_N - mg$$

$$F_N = \frac{mv^2}{r} + mg$$

$$= \frac{(75 \text{ kg})(6.0 \text{ m/s})^2}{5.0 \text{ m}} + (75 \text{ kg})(9.81 \text{ m/s}^2)$$

$$= 540 \text{ kg m/s}^2 + 735 \text{ kg m/s}^2$$

$$F_N = 1.3 \times 10^3 \text{ N}$$

so

$$F_N = \textbf{1.3} \times \textbf{10}^3 \textbf{ N, up}$$

Gravity

Kepler's Laws

Around the turn of the 16th century, an astronomer named Johannes Kepler tried to prove that the planets going around the Sun traveled on a circular path. He spent *years* trying to fit the motion he saw to a circular path, then one day, it occurred to him that maybe the planets travel on an *ellipse* (an oval). He found that this was true. He also found that the sun was at one of the two **foci** of the ellipse. We can draw an ellipse with some string and some tacks. All we have to do is tack the ends of the string down, and stretch out the pencil with the sting, as shown in the diagram below. We draw a curve with the pencil, keeping the string taut. We end up with an ellipse, and the points were the string was pinned are the foci.

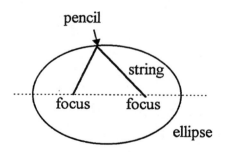

There's a lot of neat geometry involved with ellipses, but no time to go into it here. A geometry book would be your best bet for more info; check with your math teacher.

So what Kepler found after all those years of doing calculations is this:

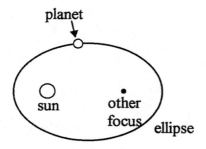

This became known as Kepler's first law. The "squishiness" (eccentricity) of the ellipse is exaggerated here. Actually, the orbits of the planets are *very* close to being circular.

Kepler's first law: The planets move around the sun in an ellipse, with the sun at one focus.

Kepler also found that the area that swept through by the sun-planet line was the same for equal times, anywhere on the ellipse. In a picture:

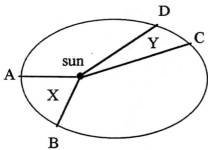

If the time it takes to go from A to B is the same as it takes to go from C to D, the areas X and Y are equal. For this to be true, the speed the planet is going has to be changing. The planet is going faster when it is close to the sun. This is Kepler's second law.

Keper's second law: The speed of the planet changes such that the line from the sun to the planet sweeps out equal areas in equal times.

We can define the **distance** (r) of the planet from the sun as the average distance over the entire orbit. The time the planet takes to go around the sun once is the **period** (T). Kepler's third law states that

$$T \propto r^{3/2},$$

the period is directly proportional to $r^{3/2}$.

Kepler's third law: $T \propto r^{3/2}$,

where T is the period, and r is the average distance from the planet to the sun.

Newton's Universal Law of Gravitation

Newton was born in 1642, twelve years after the Kepler died. Newton had some questions about gravity, and he studied Kepler's work. He knew that things near the Earth were attracted toward the Earth by the force of gravity, but he wondered how far away the force of gravity would work: the moon ? the other planets ? He used Kepler's third law, and what we know about circular motion to find his third law; the law of universal gravitation. I mentioned this when we talked about Newton's laws. Here it is again:

$$F = \frac{Gm_1 m_2}{r^2},$$

m_1 and m_2 are the masses of the two objects attracting each other, r is the distance between the two objects, and G is the **universal gravitational constant**.

About one hundred years after Newton's law of universal gravitation was discovered, Henry Cavendish proved that Newton's theory was correct. He used a very sensitive balance to measure the gravitational attraction between two balls in his laboratory. He measured very small changes in the ball's positions, and was able to find out the value of the universal gravitational constant. He found

$G = 6.673 \times 10^{-11}$ N m^2/kg.

How does G relate to g, the force of gravity near the surface of the Earth ? Let's look at something near the surface of the Earth. The gravitational force between the object and the Earth is

$$F = \frac{Gm_e m}{R_e^{\,2}},$$

where m_e is the mass of the Earth, m is the mass of the object, and R_e is the distance between the centres of the objects, which is equal to the radius of the Earth. But we also know that $F = mg$ is the force of gravity on the Earth, so

$$F = \frac{Gm_e m}{R_e^{\,2}} = mg$$

canceling the m's gives the expression for the local g in terms of G:

$$g = \frac{Gm_e}{R_e^{\,2}}$$

We can use this to find the local force of gravity for any planet. Since the local force of gravity is different for each planet, so is *weight* (*mg*).

This answered Newton's question... the force of gravity becomes weaker as the distance increases, but it's *always* there, now matter how far away you are.

Example: *How much would a 60 kg person weigh on Mercury, if Mercury has a radius of 2.51 x 10⁶ m, and a mass of 3.28 x 10²³ kg ?*

$$\text{Weight} = mg$$

and $$g = \frac{Gm_M}{R_M{}^2},$$

so $$W = m\frac{Gm_M}{R_M{}^2}$$

$$W = \frac{(60\text{ kg})\,(6.67 \times 10^{-11}\text{ N} \cdot \text{m}^2/\text{kg}^2)(3.28 \times 10^{23}\text{ kg})}{(2.57 \times 10^6\text{ m})^2}$$

W = 199 N

When we talk about the gravitational force of any object (planet, chocolate cookie), we sometimes talk about a **gravitational field**. A field is often talked about as "action at a distance". It's kind of like when your mom yells from across the apartment to turn down the CD player; you can see or touch her, but you still feel the effects of her being there. Everything in the universe is in the Earth's gravitational field. The closer an object is to the Earth, the stronger the force (the louder your mom's voice is).

Satellite Motion

The planets travel around the sun, and satellites travel around the Earth because of the Earth's gravitational field. We call things that orbit around suns and planets **satellites**. We already said that the path that planets travel around the sun is elliptical (Kepler's first), but we can make an approximation, and assume the path is circular. An approximation is when we assume a simpler case to make the calculations easier, scientists do this *a lot*. If we approximate a circular orbit, we can use the stuff we learned about uniform circular motion to talk about satellite motion. It work pretty well!

We know that the centripetal force for a satellite going around the Earth is from the Earth's gravitational field, so

$$F_c = \frac{Gm_e m}{r^2},$$

where r is the distance from the centre of the planet to the centre of the satellite. For a circular orbit, we know the centripetal force is

$$F_c = m\,\frac{v^2}{r}$$

so

$$\frac{Gm_e m}{r^2} = m\,\frac{v^2}{r}$$

the m's and one r cancel out, so we have

$$\frac{Gm_e}{r} = v^2$$

so

$$\boxed{v = \sqrt{\frac{Gm_e}{r}}}$$

This is the speed of the orbiting satellite. Since G and the mass of the Earth, m_e, are constants, the speed depends only on the radius of the orbit. The speed increases as the radius decreases. If an orbiting satellite slows down, it will drift into an orbit further away from the Earth. If it speed up, it will come closer to the Earth. Notice that the mass of the satellite isn't in the equation. An elephant and a pillow would orbit the Earth at the same speed, so long as they are at the same radius. It would just take a heck of a lot more energy to get the elephant there (not to mention an investigation from the humane society).

Since this is circular motion, we can find the **period** of the satellite. Remember that the definition for period is

$$T = \frac{2\pi r}{v}$$

and for gravitational circular motion,

$$v = \sqrt{\frac{Gm_e}{r}}$$

so

$$T = \frac{2\pi r}{\sqrt{\dfrac{Gm_e}{r}}} = \frac{2\pi r^{3/2}}{\sqrt{Gm_e}}$$

$$\boxed{T = \frac{2\pi r^{3/2}}{(Gm_e)^{1/2}}}$$

With this equation, we can use a satellite to find out how massive a planet is! If we know how far above the Earth the satellite is orbiting, and time how long it takes it to complete one revolution (one period), we can find the mass of the planet.

Example: *A satellite is propelled to an orbit of 40 000 km above the Earth's surface. The radius of the Earth is 6.38 x 10⁶ m, and the mass of the Earth is 5.98 x 10²⁴ kg. What is the satellite's orbital speed and period ?*

The orbital speed is given by

$$v = \sqrt{\frac{Gm_e}{r}},$$

where *r* is the distance from the centre of the Earth to the satellite. This is equal to the radius of the Earth plus the height of the satellite's orbit:

$$r = 6.38 \times 10^6 \text{ m} + 40000 \times 10^3 \text{ m}$$

$$= 6.38 \times 10^6 \text{ m} + 40.000 \times 10^6 \text{ m}$$

$$= 46.38 \times 10^6 \text{ m}$$

so

$$v = \sqrt{\frac{(6.67 \times 10^{-11} \text{ N} \cdot \text{m}^2/\text{kg}^2)(5.98 \times 10^{24}\text{kg})}{(46.38 \times 10^6 \text{ m})}}$$

$$v = 2.93 \times 10^3 \text{ m/s}$$

the period is

$$T = \frac{2\pi r}{v} = \frac{2\pi(46.38 \times 10^6 \text{ m})}{2.93 \times 10^3 \text{ m/s}}$$

$$T = 9.95 \times 10^4 \text{ s, or 27.6 hours.}$$

Example: *The Jarodians from the planet Jarod put at satellite in orbit at an altitude of 10 000 km. If the radius of the planet Jarod is 3.0 x 10⁶ m, and they find the period of the satellite is 20.0 hours, what is the mass of the planet ?*

We can use $T = \dfrac{2\pi r^{3/2}}{(Gm_J)^{1/2}}$ to find the mass by rearranging the equation.

Square both sides: $T^2 = \dfrac{4\pi^2 r^3}{Gm_j}$

so $m_j = \dfrac{4\pi^2 r^3}{GT^2}$

Now $r = 10000 \text{ km} + 3.0 \times 10^6 \text{ m}$

$= 10000 \times 10^3 \text{ m} + 3.0 \times 10^6 \text{ m}$

$= 10.000 \times 10^6 \text{ m} + 3.0 \times 10^6 \text{ m}$

$= 13.0 \times 10^6 \text{ m}$

and we want the period in seconds, so

$T = 20 \text{ hrs} \times 60 \text{ min/hr} \times 60 \text{ s/min}$

$= 7.20 \times 10^4 \text{ s}$

so

$m_j = \dfrac{4\pi^2 (13.0 \times 10^6 \, \text{m})^3}{(6.67 \times 10^{-11} \text{ N} \cdot \text{m}^2/\text{kg}^2)(7.20 \times 10^4 \, \text{s})^2}$

$m_j = \mathbf{2.51 \times 10^{23} \text{ kg}}$

In our solar system, the sun is by *far* the largest object. It is about 1000 times more massive than the largest planet (Jupiter). The sun has the largest gravitational field of the bodies in our solar system. This is

---

why the planets orbit around the sun. But remember that the planets are pretty big too, and have their own gravitational fields. The planets' gravitational fields all affect each other, and results in a force of attraction between the planets. The picture we have of these planets in nice circular orbits around the sun isn't quite true. In fact, several planets in our solar system were found by looking at the orbits of other planets. In 1785, Sir William Herschel knew where to look for the planet Uranus, because he studied the orbit of Saturn. He know there had to be a planet there in order to explain Saturn's orbit. Later, Uranus' orbit was used to find Neptune, and then Neptune's orbit was used to find Pluto.

Not only do the planets all effect each other's orbits, by the gravitational forces between galaxies effects the shape of the entire universe. The effects of gravitational fields are far reaching, and shapes the universe around us.

Gravity Practice Problems

1.(a) What's the local value of gravity on the smallest planet, Mercury ?
(mass $= 3.28 \times 10^{23}$ kg, radius $= 2.57 \times 10^6$ m)

(b) What's the local value of gravity on the largest planet, Jupiter ?
(mass $= 1.90 \times 10^{27}$ kg, radius $= 7.18 \times 10^7$ m)

(c) What's the gravitational attraction between Mercury and Jupiter if they're separated by 7.04×10^{11} m ?

---

2. (a) What's the force of attraction between a ball (mass = 0.20 kg) and the earth ?

(b) What's the force of attraction between the ball and a 1000 kg truck 1 m away ?

3.(a) What's the speed of the Hubble telescope if it's in orbit 596 km above the earth ? (mass of earth $= 5.98 \times 10^{24}$ kg, radius of earth $= 6.38 \times 10^{6}$ m)

3. (b) What's the period ?

4. In an alternate dimension, the universal gravitational constant is different. You get warped into this dimension (probably by some transporter malfunction), and find G by sending up a satellite. You know $r = 7.00 \times 10^6$ m, mass of the planet $= 6.00 \times 10^{24}$ kg, and it takes the satellite 3 hours to orbit the planet once. Find G, and prove the units for G are the same in both dimensions.

PHYSICS GRADE 11

Gravity Practice Problem Solutions

1.(a) *What's the local value of gravity on the smallest planet, Mercury ?*
(mass = 3.28 × 10²³ kg, radius = 2.57 × 10⁶ m)

$$g = \frac{Gm_{M}}{R_{M}^{2}}$$

$$= \frac{(6.67 \times 10^{-11} \ \text{N} \cdot \text{m}^{2}/\text{kg}^{2})(3.28 \times 10^{23} \ \text{kg})}{(2.57 \times 10^{6} \text{m})^{2}}$$

$$g = 3.3 \ \text{m/s}^{2}$$

(b) What's the local value of gravity on the largest planet, Jupiter ?
(mass =1.90 × 10²⁷ kg, radius = 7.18 × 10⁷ m)

$$g = \frac{Gm_{J}}{R_{J}^{2}}$$

$$= \frac{(6.67 \times 10^{-11} \ \text{N} \cdot \text{m}^{2}/\text{kg}^{2})(1.90 \times 10^{27} \ \text{kg})}{(7.18 \times 10^{7} \text{m})^{2}}$$

$$g = 24.6 \ \text{m/s}^{2}$$

(c) What's the gravitational attraction between Mercury and Jupiter if they're separated by 7.04 × 10¹¹ m ?

$$F_{g} = \frac{Gm_{J}m_{M}}{r^{2}}$$

$$= \frac{(6.67 \times 10^{-11} \ \text{N} \cdot \text{m}^{2}/\text{kg}^{2})(1.90 \times 10^{27} \ \text{kg})(3.28 \times 10^{23} \ \text{kg})}{(7.04 \times 10^{11} \text{m})^{2}}$$

$$F_{g} = 8.39 \times 10^{16} \ \text{N} \text{ is the attractive force between them.}$$

---

2. (a) *What's the force of attraction between a ball (mass = 0.20 kg) and the earth ?*

$$F_g = mg = (0.20 \text{ kg})(9.81 \text{ m/s}^2) = \textbf{2.0 N}$$

(b) *What's the force of attraction between the ball and a 1000 kg truck 1 m away ?*

$$F_g = \frac{Gm_1 m_2}{r^2}$$

$$= \frac{(6.67 \times 10^{-11} \text{ N} \cdot \text{m}^2/\text{kg}^2)(0.20 \text{ kg})(1000 \text{ kg})}{(1 \text{ m})^2}$$

$$F_g = \textbf{1.3} \times \textbf{10}^{-8} \textbf{ N}$$

You can see why the ball falls *down*, and not across to the truck.

3. (a) *What's the speed of the Hubble telescope if it's in orbit 596 km above the earth ? (mass of earth = 5.98 × 10²⁴ kg, radius of earth = 6.38 × 10⁶ m)*

Use $$v = \sqrt{\frac{Gm_e}{r}}\, ,$$

where r is the distance from the centre of the Earth to the satellite. This is equal to the radius of the Earth plus the height of the satellite's orbit:

$$r = 6.38 \times 10^6 \text{ m} + 596 \times 10^3 \text{ m}$$

$$= 6.38 \times 10^6 \text{ m} + 0.596 \times 10^6 \text{ m}$$

$$= 6.98 \times 10^6 \text{ m}$$

so $$v = \sqrt{\frac{(6.67 \times 10^{-11} \text{ N} \cdot \text{m}^2/\text{kg}^2)(5.98 \times 10^{24} \text{kg})}{(6.98 \times 10^6 \text{ m})}}$$

$$v = \textbf{7.56 x 10}^3 \textbf{ m/s}$$

3. (b) What's the period ?

The period is $T=\dfrac{2\pi r}{v}=\dfrac{2\pi(6.98\times10^6\text{ m})}{7.56\times10^3\text{ m/s}}=5.80\times10^3\text{ s}$

$T = 5.80\times10^3$ s, or 1.6 hours.

4. In an alternate dimension, the universal gravitational constant is different. You get warped into this dimension (probably by some transporter malfunction), and find G by sending up a satellite. You know $r = 7.00\times10^6$ m, mass of the planet = 6.00×10^{24} kg, and it takes the satellite 3 hours to orbit the planet once. Find G, and prove the units for G are the same in both dimensions.

$3\text{ hours} = 3\text{ hr}\times3600\text{ s/hr} = 1.08\times10^3\text{ s}$

We can use $T=\dfrac{2\pi r^{3/2}}{(Gm)^{1/2}}$ to find G, by rearranging the equation.

Square both sides:

$$T^2=\frac{4\pi^2 r^3}{Gm}$$

$$G=\frac{4\pi^2 r^3}{T^2 m}=\frac{4\pi^2(7.00\times10^6\text{m})^3}{(1.08\times10^3\text{s})^2(6.00\times10^{24}\text{kg})}$$
$$G=6.61\times10^{-10}\text{ m}^3/\text{s}^2\text{ kg}$$

Check to see if these are the same units...

In our universe, the units we have been using for G are $\dfrac{N\cdot m^2}{kg^2}$,

so $\dfrac{N\cdot m^2}{kg^2}=\dfrac{\frac{kg\cdot m}{s^2}\cdot m^2}{kg^2}=\dfrac{kg\cdot m^3}{s^2\cdot kg^2}=\dfrac{m^3}{s^2\cdot kg}$, which are the

units we found above.

PHYSICS GRADE 11

Simple Harmonic Motion and Wave Motion

Simple Harmonic Motion

When you see a spring bounce up and down, or a clock pendulum swing back and forth, you are watching simple harmonic motion.

> **Simple Harmonic Motion (SHM)** is an acceleration towards a fixed point, due to a restoring force. The restoring force is proportional to the displacement from the equilibrium position.

Basically, all this says is that things that bounce up and down (you on your bed, or a bungee jumper) or swing back and forth (a clock pendulum, or a kid on a swing) are simple harmonic motions. Let's look at the definition again, this time talking about a ball on a spring.

If we push on a spring to compress it, then let go, you know what will happen; the spring will bounce back and forth for a while until it eventually stops (due to friction). This bouncing is called **vibration**, or **oscillation**. When we push or pull the spring from its **equilibrium position** (also called the 0 position or rest position; it's the position it takes if you don't mess with it), we apply a force.

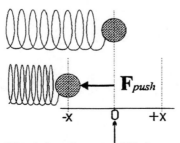

The 0 (zero), or equilibrium position - where it is if you don't push on the spring

---

When we release the spring, there is a **restoring force** that accelerates the spring back toward its equilibrium position. The same thing happens if we pull on the spring. This is the "acceleration towards a fixed point, due to a restoring force" in the definition.

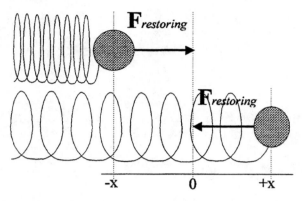

For small compressions, this force is proportional to the displacement (x) of the spring, so

$$F = -kx$$

where k is a constant of proportionality, called the **spring constant**. It is negative because the force is always in the opposite direction of the displacement. This is the "restoring force is proportional to the displacement from the equilibrium position" part of the definition. It is know as **Hooke's law**.

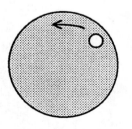

top: see
uniform circular
motion

Now, put a ball just like the one on the end of the spring on a uniformly spinning turntable. When we look at it from the top, we see uniform circular motion. Now look at it from the side, with your line of sight parallel to the top of the turn table, like this:

eye ◁────────── ○ ──turntable

What your eye will see from the side view is pretty much the same thing you saw with the oscillating spring. You see the ball apparently bounce back and forth!

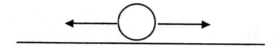

Uniform circular motion and simple harmonic motion have many similarities.

Displacement

In SHM, the displacement (x) is how far an object is from the equilibrium position (0).

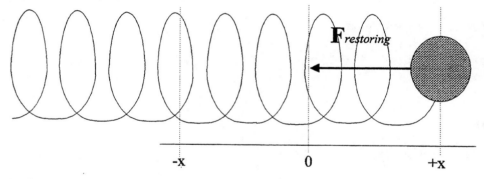

Speed and Velocity

In simple harmonic motion, like with the spring, the speed is *not* constant, so neither is the velocity. This is different from uniform circular motion, like the turntable, where the velocity is changing, but the speed is constant.

In SHM, the speed and velocity are zero at the maximum displacement. The speed and velocity are at maximums when the object passes through the equilibrium point.

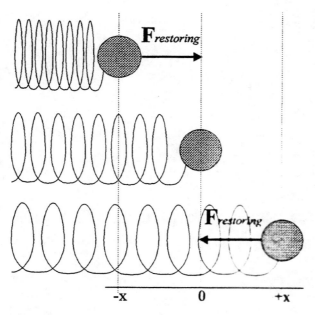

at maximum compression, $v=0$

at equilibrium position, v=maximum

at maximum extension, $v=0$

-x   0   +x

Acceleration

In both simple harmonic motion, and uniform circular motion we have an acceleration directed towards a fixed point. For circular motion, it's toward the centre of the circle, and for SHM, it's toward the equilibrium position (the opposite direction of the displacement).

Period

Remember that we defined a period in circular motion as *one* revolution around the circle. We can use this definition to define a period in SHM. Let's look at the ball on the turntable again. We let the ball go through one period, starting on the right, as in the left hand diagram below. As we look at the ball's motion from the side, we see the motion drawn in the right hand diagram.

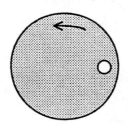

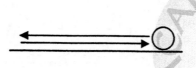

The ball in the right hand diagram appears to travel all the way to the left, and then back again. In simple harmonic motion, the *period is the time it takes for the object to return to the original position, or one complete oscillation.*

Conservation of Energy and Simple Harmonic Motion

One of the easiest ways to analyze simple harmonic motion is to apply what we learned about the conservation of mechanical energy. Remember that we said the kinetic energy plus the potential energy of an object in motion is constant (ignoring frictional forces), or

$$TE = KE + PE = constant$$

When a spring is stretched, or compressed, it has stored potential energy, and the kinetic energy is zero (since $v = 0$). When you release it, this potential energy is transformed into kinetic energy, and then as it compresses (or stretches) again, it is converted into potential energy again.

0

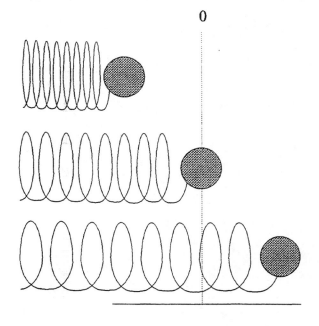

max. compression:
$v=0$
$KE=0$
$PE=max.$

through 0 point:
$v=max.$
$KE=max.$
$PE=0$

max. extension:
$v=0$
$KE=0$
$PE=max.$

Simple Harmonic Motion and Wave Motion

The same idea works for other objects showing SHM, a pendulum, for example. In this case, the potential energy is gravitational potential energy (measured from the minimum height of the pendulum, when it's just hanging). The PE is at a maximum when the height is at a maximum, at the end of each swing, and the KE is at a maximum as its passes through the middle point.

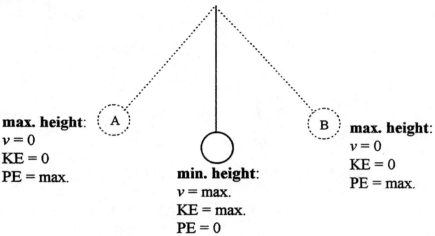

max. height:
$v = 0$
KE = 0
PE = max.

min. height:
$v = $ max.
KE = max.
PE = 0

max. height:
$v = 0$
KE = 0
PE = max.

Just like for the spring, the period is the time it takes for the pendulum mass to return to complete one oscillation. In the diagram above, it's the time the mass would take to return to position A, starting from A, or to return to position B, if it started at B.

Example: *Andrew and Lori want to use a 10 kg pendulum to break down a door. Lori guesses that the pendulum will have to have 1000 J of energy to do the job, and it will contact the door at the end of the first swing, as in the picture below. If we assume that all the mechanical energy the pendulum has is given up to the door on impact, what is the maximum speed will the mass reach? How high off the floor should Lori release the mass?*

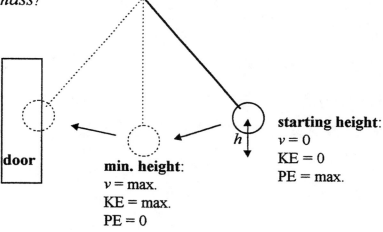

Find the maximum velocity is easy! We know the TE = 1000 J, and at the bottom of the swing (at min. height), TE = KE.

$$TE = KE = \frac{1}{2}mv^2$$

so
$$TE = \frac{1}{2}mv^2$$

and so
$$v = \sqrt{\frac{2\,TE}{m}} = \sqrt{\frac{2\,(1000\ J)}{10\ kg}} = \textbf{14 m/s}$$

It isn't any harder to find the height they need. Before they release the mass, it has only PE, so PE = TE = 1000 J.

recall
$$PE = mgh$$

so
$$h = \frac{PE}{mg} = \frac{1000\ J}{(10\ kg)(9.81\ m/s^2)} = \textbf{10 m}$$

They need to release the 10 kg mass 10 m above the lowest point of the swing. Maybe they should find a heavier mass!

Resonance

If we start an object oscillating, either a spring or a pendulum, if we ignore friction, the mass will oscillate forever. What would happen if instead of giving the mass a push or a pull and letting go, we kept applying the force ? We could do this by pushing and pulling along with the oscillations. This continued force is called a **driving force**, and the type of motion that come from doing this is called **driven harmonic motion.** A good example would be giving a push to someone on a swing every time they reach you - they go higher with each pass. What we're doing is increasing the amount of energy in the system.

Now, a spring or a pendulum will have a rate it likes to go, a **natural frequency**. The period of a particular spring or pendulum is always the same. If the driving force applied is the same frequency (remember that frequency = 1/T), more and more energy is added to the system, and the displacement of the mass will keep getting larger and larger! When this happens, you have resonance.

Driving force: A continued force applied to an oscillating system.
Natural frequency: The frequency at which an oscillating system will oscillate, if there is no driving force applied.
Resonance happens when a oscillating driving force transmits large amounts of energy to an oscillating object, which results in an increasing amplitude (displacement). The applied force needs to oscillate at a natural frequency for resonance to happen.

Designers always have to take resonance into account in their designs. It's not only springs that can experience resonance. Loudspeakers, for example, have a diaphragm that oscillates with the sound. The diaphragm will vibrate with a much larger amplitude at the natural frequency of the diaphragm. If the speaker wasn't designed with this in mind, one note will sound a lot louder than the others. The music coming through would get pretty badly garbled. Sometimes resonance can cause a lot more damage than bad sound. There's film footage of the collapse of the Tacoma Narrows bridge, in Washington state. It collapsed because the wind whipped across it at the natural frequency of the bridge! (This is a really great film to see! Ask your teacher if (s)he can get it to show you.) Another example that comes to mind happened in a dance club. Lots of people were dancing on a catwalk, and they all started to dance to the music, but it was at the natural frequency of the catwalk. The catwalk collapsed under them.

Simple Harmonic Motion of Particles

We're going to go back to our horizontal mass oscillating on the end of a spring. This time, we're going to attach a pen to the mass, like in the picture below, and scroll some paper by the pen at a constant speed.

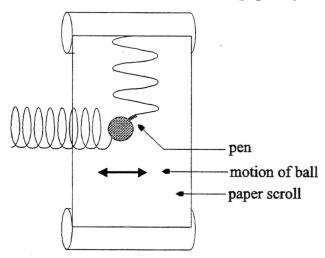

pen

motion of ball

paper scroll

We see the pattern that is drawn in the picture. You might notice that this looks like water waves. It's what we call a **waveform**, and tells us something about how particles move through space. In this example, the ball represents the particle, and it is oscillating to the left and right while the

paper is scrolled. We would get the same pattern if we moved the
oscillating ball down as it bounced to the right and left, but didn't move
the paper. This is basically what's going on when particles travel through
space. Like this:

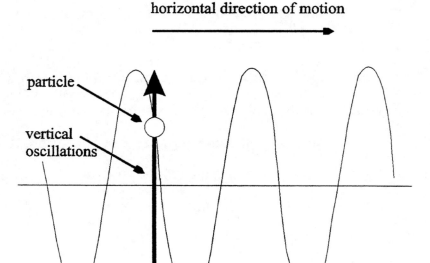

The particle is moving in two directions, but the *net movement* is to the
right. *When particles travel through space, they undergo simple*
harmonic oscillations perpendicular to the net direction of travel.

PHYSICS GRADE 11

Simple Harmonic Motion and Wave Motion Practice Problems

1. The diagram below shows the same spring at three different extensions. If x is the maximum displacement of the spring, label the equilibrium position, the maximum and minimum speeds, maximum and minimum acceleration, and maximum and minimum restoring force. Draw arrows to indicate the direction of the acceleration and restoring force.

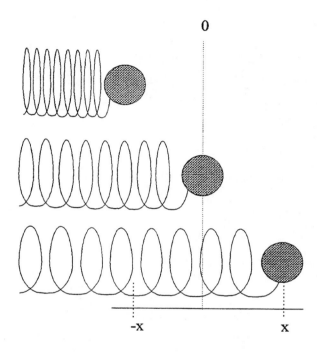

2. Two identical springs are stretched. One is stretched 10 cm, and the other 12 cm. Which will exert a larger restoring force ? Why ?

3. Musicians use metronomes to time beats while practicing. A metronome is a rod with a weight that will slide up and down, with the bottom fixed. The rod oscillates back and forth, like an upside down pendulum. If it takes 0.75 s for the rod to go from the far left to the far right, what is the frequency of the metronome ?

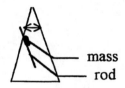

4. We compress a spring with a 0.53 kg mass on the end, giving it a potential energy of 13 J. Assuming the spring itself is massless, what will be the maximum speed of the mass ?

Simple Harmonic Motion and Wave Motion Practice Problem Solutions

1. The diagram below shows the same spring at three different extensions. If x is the maximum displacement of the spring, label the equilibrium position, the maximum and minimum speeds, maximum and minimum acceleration, and maximum and minimum restoring force. Draw arrows to indicate the direction of the acceleration and restoring force.

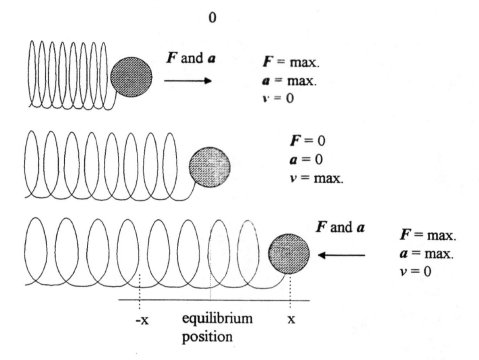

0

F and **a**

F = max.
a = max.
$v = 0$

$F = 0$
$a = 0$
v = max.

F and **a**

F = max.
a = max.
$v = 0$

-x   equilibrium   x
      position

2. *Two identical springs are stretched. One is stretched 10 cm, and the other 12 cm. Which will exert a larger restoring force ? Why ?*

The one stretched 12 cm exerts a greater restoring force, since the displacement is greater. For simple harmonic motion, the restoring force is proportional to the displacement.

3. *Musicians use metronomes to time beats while practicing. A metronome is a rod with a weight that will slide up and down, with the bottom fixed. The rod oscillates back and forth, like an upside down pendulum. If it takes 0.75 s for the rod to go from the far left to the far right, what is the frequency of the metronome ?*

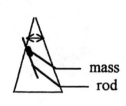

The period , T is

$$T = 2 \times 0.75 \text{ s} = 1.50 \text{ s}$$

mass
rod

Frequency is $f = 1/T$,

$$f = 1/T = 1/(1.50 \text{ s}) = \textbf{0.67 Hz}$$

4. *We compress a spring with a 0.53 kg mass on the end, giving it a potential energy of 13 J. Assuming the spring itself is massless, what will be the maximum speed of the mass ?*

The maximum speed will be when the mass passes through the equilibrium point, where PE = 0, so all the energy is KE.

$$PE_i = KE_{max}$$

so

$$13 \text{ J} = \frac{1}{2} m v_{max}^2$$

and

$$v_{max}^2 = \frac{2 (13 \text{ J})}{m}$$

$$v_{max} = \sqrt{\frac{2 (13 \text{ J})}{0.53 \text{ kg}}} = \textbf{7.0 m/s}$$

PHYSICS GRADE 11
Mechanical Waves

What are waves, anyway? We all know what water waves are, but there are other kinds too: sound waves, and particle waves are a couple of examples. There are two criteria for something to be a wave. First, a wave is a traveling **disturbance** (a shape, form, or pattern). Second, a wave carries energy, and can move the energy it carries from place to place. Waves are a very important way that energy gets moved around in our world.

A good question is "how does the wave move around ?" Waves usually have to have a **medium**. A medium is what the wave moves (**propagates**) through. For water waves, the medium is water. For sound waves, the medium is air. If the medium isn't there, that kind of wave can't happen. This is why there is no sound in outer space (no matter what they have on Star Trek). In outer space, there's no air, so no medium through which the sound waves can propagate. In the case of sound waves, it's the molecules in the air that vibrate which cause the waves. The same thing is true for any wave that travels through a medium; *the medium particle vibrations carry the wave.* One particle pulls (or pushes) the next particle, which transfers the energy the first particle had to the second.

This is quite different from the way we've talked about energy transfer in earlier sections. For example, if car 1 hits car 2, car 1 will give energy to car 2. Car 1 is the energy source and car 2 is the energy receiver. Transfer of energy is different with waves. The energy source and receiver don't have to touch each other, since the energy is propagated by the medium, to the recipient.

Transverse and Longitudinal Waves

There are two basic kinds of waves, transverse, and longitudinal. In a transverse wave, the particles vibrate in a direction perpendicular to the direction of propagation (the net direction of motion). A good way to see this is too raise and lower the end of a Slinky (a long, loose coil) in simple harmonic motion. Here, the Slinky is the medium of propagation, and we can think of each coil as a medium "particle". The simple harmonic motion at the end cause waves that will travel to the other end of the Slinky, like this

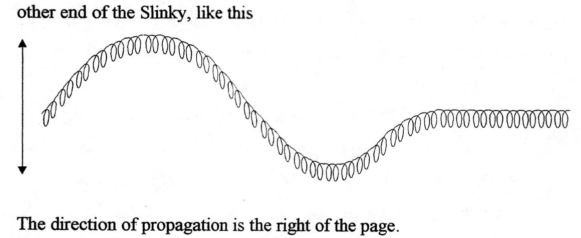

The direction of propagation is the right of the page.

If we tie a string around one of the coils, and watch to see how it moves, we see that it only goes up and down, like this

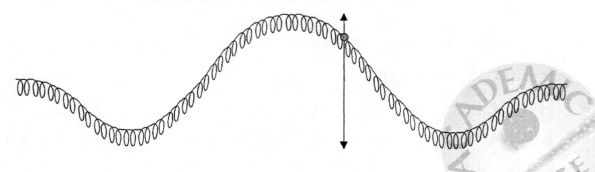

The direction of propagation is the right of the page, but the motion of the particles (each coil) is up and down.

> A **transverse wave** is a wave where the direction of propagation is perpendicular to the direction of the particle vibration.

Longitudinal waves (also called compression waves) are waves where the direction of propagation and the direction of particle vibration are the same. Let's look at the Slinky again. We compress a bunch of coils at one end of the Slinky by pushing (this makes a **compression**), and then pull the end back to the original position. Pulling the end back makes a region of stretched coils (a **rarefaction**) right after the compression, like this

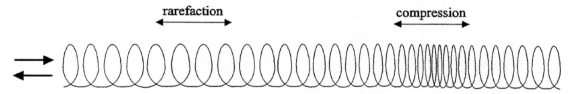

We keep pushing and pulling in simple harmonic motion, and we soon get a longitudinal wave traveling to the right side of the page.

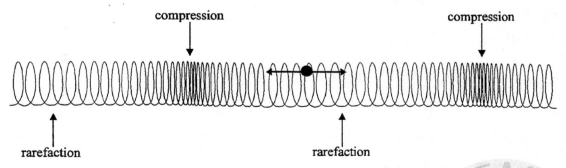

We can tie a bit of string to one of the coil again, and see that this time, the individual coils are vibrating to the left and right.

A **longitudinal** (or **compression**) **wave** is a wave where the direction of propagation is parallel to the direction of particle vibration.

Waves are often pictured like this: a waveform. You already saw a waveform at the end of the simple harmonic motion section.

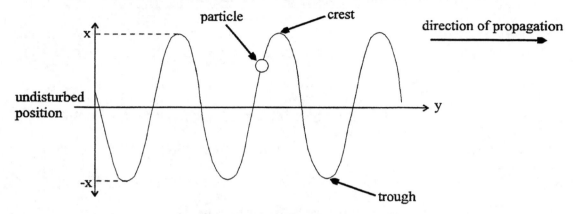

The peaks are called **crests**, and the dips are called **troughs**.

The x-axis shows the simple harmonic vibration of the medium particles (or Slinky coils). The y-axis shows us the wave's displacement, or how far it has propagated. The line through the middle of the waveform is the particle's undisturbed position. This is where the particle would be sitting if it wasn't vibrating.

Wavelength and Amplitude

We often want to know how big the waves are. If you like to surf, you want to know whether you should bother driving out to the beach. We talk about wave size in terms of wavelength and amplitude. The amplitude (A) is the size of the particle vibration. It's measured from the undisturbed position to the wave crest or trough, as shown here.

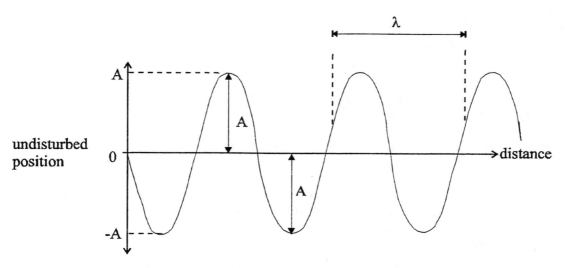

The wavelength (λ - the Greek letter "lambda") is one cycle of vibration. It is measured from crest to crest, from trough to trough, or like in the picture here, from one undisturbed position to the *second* one after.

Period and Frequency

The **period**, T, of a waveform is defined the same way as a period in simple harmonic motion, or circular motion. It's the time it takes to go through one cycle. We can also say it's the time it takes to complete one wavelength, measured in *seconds*.

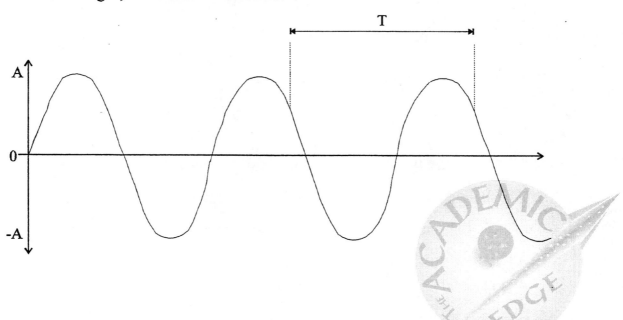

The **frequency**, f, is the number of cycles/second, just like for simple harmonic motion.

$$f = \frac{1}{T},$$

Remember that the unit for frequency is 1/s, or Hz.

The source of the wave is what decides the wave's frequency. The faster you whip the Slinky around, the higher the frequency of the waves. You'll get a lower frequency sound wave by singing a low note, than if you sang a high one. The frequency *doesn't* depend on how *loud* you sing.

Wave Speed

What decides how fast the wave will go ? Let's look at what makes a wave propagate by looking at someone making waves in a string. In the picture, I've drawn in some medium particles (the particles are just short segments of the string).

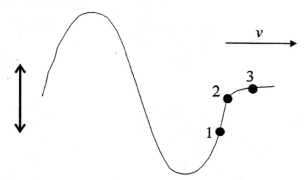

In the picture, the wave hasn't reached particle #3 yet. How does it get there? Particle #1 will pull on particle #2, which will in turn pull on particle #3. The harder #1 pulls on #2 (the greater the force), the faster the wave will be transmitted, because the acceleration will be larger ($F = ma$).

What determined how hard #1 can pull on #2? One factor is the strength of the source, but another one is how tight the string is stretched (or how taut the coils of the Slinky are pulled). It also depends the weight of each of the particles A thick string would have a slower wave speed than a thin one made of the same stuff. Because of $F = ma$, a heavier particle needs a larger force to get the same acceleration as a lighter particle. *A wave's speed depends on the medium of propagation.*

It's easy to find out how fast a wave is traveling. We can use the definition of speed:

$$\text{speed} = \frac{\text{distance}}{\text{time}}$$

Since a wave travels a distance of one wavelength, λ, in one period, T:

$$v = \frac{d}{t} = \frac{\lambda}{T} = \lambda \frac{1}{T}$$

and since

$$f = \frac{1}{T}$$

then

$$\boxed{v = \lambda f}$$

This is true for both longitudinal and transverse waves.

If we increase either, or both, of the source frequency, and the wavelength, the wave will propagate faster.

Example: *Compare the wavelengths of an AM radiowave of 700 kHz, and FM radiowave of 90 Mhz. The speed of the waves through air is 3.00×10^8 m/s.*

We know the speed of the waves, and the frequencies, so we can use $v = f\lambda$ to find the wavelengths.

$$v = f\lambda$$

$$\lambda = \frac{v}{f}$$

AM radio: $700 \text{ kHz} = 700 \times 10^3 \text{ Hz}$

$$\lambda = \frac{v}{f} = \frac{3.00 \times 10^8 \text{ m/s}}{700 \times 10^3 \text{ Hz}} = \textbf{429 m}$$

FM radio: $90 \text{ MHz} = 90 \times 10^6 \text{ Hz}$

$$\lambda = \frac{v}{f} = \frac{3.00 \times 10^8 \text{ m/s}}{90 \times 10^6 \text{ Hz}} = \textbf{3.3 m}$$

AM radio waves have a *huge* wavelength when compared to FM radio waves.

The Doppler Effect

If you've ever heard a vehicle with a siren running drive past, you may have noticed that the sound of the siren seems to change. It has a higher pitch when it's coming toward you that when it is driving away. I used to wonder why it sounded like that, but then I learned about the Doppler effect.

> **The Doppler effect**: When either the wave source, or the observer (who or what is hearing the sound) is moving with respect to the medium of sound propagation, the observer will detect a change in frequency.

If the source of the noise (like a siren) is still, the sound waves look like this:

Stationary Observer and Stationary Source

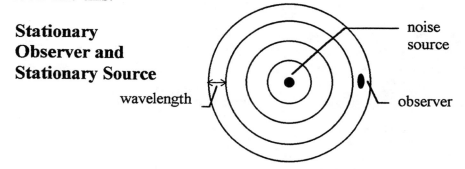

The wavelengths of the propagating waves are the same all around the source. No matter where the observer stands, she will hear the same frequency. Now, if the source starts to move, the waves look like this:

Stationary Observer and Moving Source

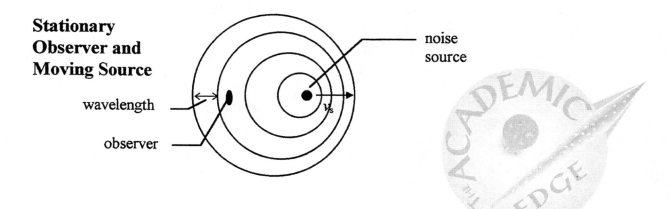

The wavelength is smaller ahead of the moving source, and bigger behind. The waves bunch up ahead of the source because the source is moving with respect to the air, so it starts to catch up to the waves already emitted. The waves are further apart behind the source because the source is traveling away from these already emitted waves. Since the wavelength is *smaller* ahead of the moving source, an observer standing in front of the source would hear a *higher* frequency than if the source were stationary. Since the wavelength behind the moving source is *larger*, an observer watching the source move away would hear a *lower* frequency than if the source were stationary.

How *much* does the frequency change ? We know that the source emits a wave every period, so at every time T, but in this time T, the source have moved a distance (remember $d = vt$) $v_s T$, where v_s is the speed of the moving source. So the new distance between the waves ahead of the source is the difference between the wavelength and the distance the source has moved, or

$$\lambda' = \lambda - v_s T,$$

where λ' is the new wavelength. Remember that $v = f\lambda$, so the new frequency ahead of the source is, f', is

$$f' = \frac{v}{\lambda'} = \frac{v}{\lambda - v_s T}$$

where v is the speed of sound (343 m/s). We can substitute in $\lambda = v/f$, and $T = 1/f$ in this equation, and get

$$f' = \cfrac{v}{\cfrac{v}{f} - v_s \cfrac{1}{f}} = \cfrac{v}{\cfrac{v - v_s}{f}} = f \cfrac{v}{v - v_s} = f \cfrac{\cfrac{v}{v}}{\cfrac{v}{v} - \cfrac{v_s}{v}} = f \cfrac{1}{1 - \cfrac{v_s}{v}}$$

The frequency heard by a stationary observer from an approaching sound source is

$$\boxed{f' = f \cfrac{1}{1 - \cfrac{v_s}{v}}}$$

The difference between f' and f is called the Doppler shift.

Doppler shift: The difference between the frequency emitted by a source, and the frequency observed:

$$\text{Doppler shift} = f' - f$$

We can find the frequency heard by an observer standing behind the moving source almost exactly the same way. The only difference is that the new distance between the waves *behind* the source is the old wavelength plus the distance the source has moved, or

$$\lambda' = \lambda + v_s T,$$

we follow exactly the same method as above and find $f' = f \cfrac{1}{1 + \cfrac{v_s}{v}}$.

The frequency heard by a stationary observer from a sound source moving away is

$$\boxed{f' = f \cfrac{1}{1 + \cfrac{v_s}{v}}}$$

Example: *A bird flying past Franklin at 10 m/s, and lets out a 400 Hz cry. The speed of sound is 343 m/s. What frequency does he hear as the bird is approaching ? What frequency does he hear as the bird is flying away ? What is the Doppler shift in each case ?*

As the bird is *approaching*, he hears a frequency of

$$f' = f \frac{1}{1 - \dfrac{v_s}{v}} = (400 \text{ Hz}) \frac{1}{1 - \dfrac{11 \text{ m/s}}{343 \text{ m/s}}} = \textbf{413 Hz}$$

so the Doppler shift is $f' - f = 413 \text{ Hz} - 400 \text{ Hz} = \textbf{13 Hz}$

As the bird is *flying away*, he hears a frequency of

$$f' = f \frac{1}{1 + \dfrac{v_s}{v}} = (400 \text{ Hz}) \frac{1}{1 + \dfrac{11 \text{ m/s}}{343 \text{ m/s}}} = \textbf{388 Hz}$$

so the Doppler shift is $f' - f = 388 \text{ Hz} - 400 \text{ Hz} = \textbf{-12 Hz}$

Notice that the Doppler shift is nearly the same for the source approaching as for the source moving away, except for the negative sign.

Now, what if the *source* is stationary, and it's the *observer* that's moving ?

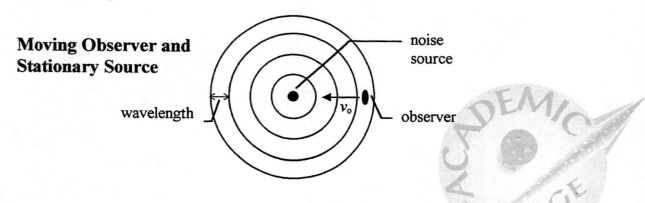

Moving Observer and Stationary Source

wavelength

noise source

v_o

observer

In this picture, the observer is moving toward the source, and the sound waves are moving toward the observer. The observer will hear all the sound waves that a stationary observer would, and *more*, since he's moving toward the source. How many more ? We can find this by taking the distance he's moved ($v_o t$) divided by the distance between waves (λ), or $v_o t/\lambda$. So in one second, this would be v_o/λ. So the frequency the observer hears as he approaches the stationary source is:

$$f' = f + \frac{v_o}{\lambda}$$

so

$$f' = f\left(1 + \frac{v_o}{f\lambda}\right)$$

we can substitute into $\lambda = v/f$ this equation, and get

$$f' = f\left(1 + \frac{v_o}{f\frac{v}{f}}\right) = f\left(1 + \frac{v_o}{v}\right)$$

The frequency an observer hears when moving toward a stationary

source is

$$\boxed{f' = f\left(1 + \frac{v_o}{v}\right)}$$

When the observer is moving away from the stationary source, he will hear fewer waves, so we have

$$f' = f - \frac{v_o}{\lambda}.$$

We can then find the equation the exact same way is we just did when the observer was moving toward the source.

The frequency an observer hears when moving away from a stationary source is

$$f' = f\left(1 - \frac{v_0}{v}\right)$$

When the *source* is moving, and the observer isn't, the actual wavelength and frequency changes (the waves become squished and stretched out). When the *observer* is moving, and the source isn't, the wavelength and frequency is the same, it's just that the observer moves through a different number of waves. Moving through a greater or smaller number of waves makes it seem like the wavelength and frequency have changed.

Wave Reflection and Transmission

What happens when a wave hits another medium ? We call a change in medium a **boundary**. We can do some simple experiments to see what happens to waves at boundaries by making some **pulses** in a string. A pulse is one wave, or half a wave, like this

First, we'll look at what happens if the boundary leads to a medium that won't propagate the waves. We can tie the string to a door knob, and send a pulse, like this,

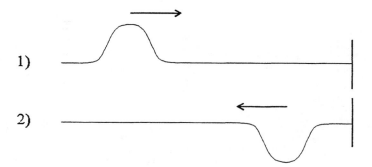

In the second picture, we see what happens. The pulse hits the wall, and bounces back with the same amplitude, but it's upside down. *A wave is reflected at a fixed end, and the reflected wave is inverted.*

Now, instead of the wall, we'll tie a heavier string to the end of the first string.

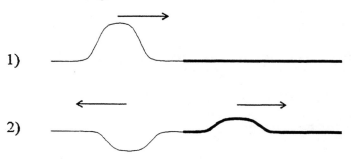

This time, part of the wave is reflected (and inverted), and part of the wave is transmitted to the heavy string. The transmitted pulse is right side up, but the amplitude is split between the reflected and transmitted pulses. In fact, if we played around with the weights of the strings, we would find that *the heavier the second string, the smaller the amplitude of the transmitted wave.* If we tie a thread to a heavy rope, and send a pulse down the thread, all the pulse will be reflected, and none transmitted.

What will happen if we send the pulse down the *heavy* string, instead of the lighter one ?

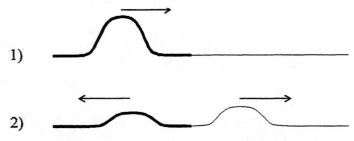

1)

2)

Part of the pulse is reflected, but this time, the reflected part is right side up! The transmitted part is right side up, and both pulses have a smaller amplitude. *As the second string is made lighter, the reflected pulse gets larger.* If we tie a heavy rope to the end of a thread, and send a pulse down the heavy rope, almost all of the pulse will be reflected, and almost none transmitted.

How are two-dimensional waves reflected, like water waves ? We can look at waves in a swimming pool hitting the side at an angle. We can draw a normal line (a line perpendicular to the surface) at the point where a wave hits the side, like this:

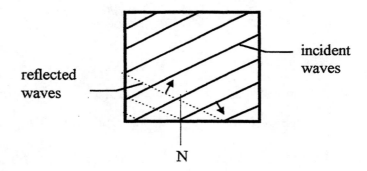

We find that *the angle between the reflected wave and the normal line is the same as between the incident wave and the normal line.*

Wave Refraction

You may remember that I mentioned that the speed of wave propagation depend on the medium. You also might remember that the frequency of the source determines the frequency of the wave, not the medium. If we look at $v = f\lambda$, and keep the frequency constant across a boundary, we can see that it has to be the *wavelength* that changes to cause the change in wave speed.

We can see an example of this in a swimming pool which has a sudden increase in depth. A change in the depth of the water can be seen as a change in the medium. When the pool gets deeper, the wavelength of the waves gets *larger*, but the frequency is the same all the way across the pool.

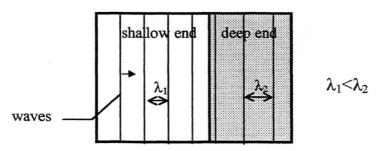

What if the waves come at the boundary between the shallow and deep regions at an angle ?

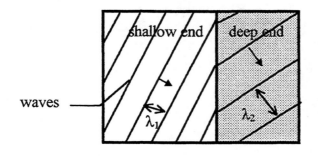

The wavelength changes as it did before, but the waves all change their direction of propagation, they are **refracted**.

The Superposition Principle

What happens if two waves meet each other ? Do they get mashed together, cancel each other out, or what ? If we send two pulses with equal amplitudes toward each other, this is what we see:

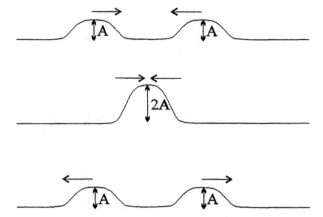

The pulse overlap, and when they meet at the middle, they combine to form one pulse with twice the amplitude. Finally, they pass through each other, each with the same shape and amplitude it started with. Let's look at another example: this time, the amplitudes are the same, but one pulse is upside down.

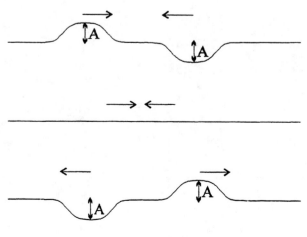

The pulses add together to form a **resultant** pulse. This is an example of the principle of linear superposition.

Principle of linear superposition: When two or more waves meet, the resultant wave is the sum of the individual waves.

In this section, we only talked about the superposition of pulses, which are very simple disturbances. An important thing to remember is that the principle of superposition is true for *all* waves, including sound waves, water waves, waves in strings or coils, and any other kinds of waves you can think of.

Interference

Now that we know the principle of superposition, we can talk about some more complicated cases of waves overlapping, called **interference**. Interference happens when two waves like sound waves, or water waves superimpose. Since these waves are made of many pulses (not just one, like in the last section), the superposition pattern can be more complicated.

Let's look a the waves coming from two speakers. The frequency coming from each of the speakers is the same, so the wavelength is the same, and when speaker 1 sends out a wave crest, speaker 2 also sends out a wave crest. Similarly, when speaker 1 sends out a trough, speaker 2 sends out a trough. Pictured on the following page is someone listening to the music, sitting at as far away from the first speaker as the second.

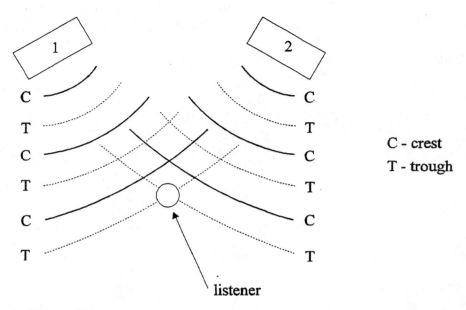

C - crest
T - trough

In this position, the troughs from speaker 1 reach the listener at the same time as the troughs from speaker 2. The same thing goes for the crests. Remembering the principle of superposition,

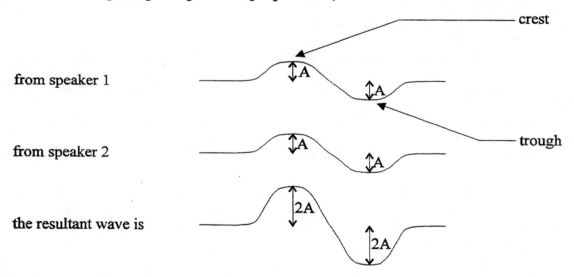

This means that the amplitude of the resultant wave is *twice* as big as the individual waves, and the music will sound twice as loud as if there was only one speaker! This is constructive interference, and the waves are **in phase** (crest-to-crest and trough-to-trough).

PHYSICS GRADE 11

Now the listener moves closer to one speaker, so that the crest from speaker 1 gets to him at the same time as the trough from speaker 2.

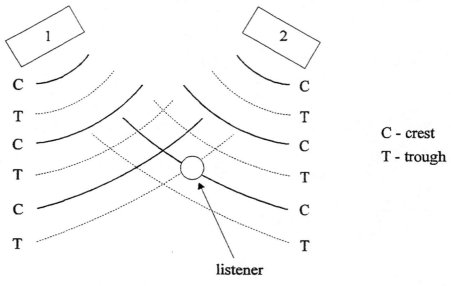

C - crest

T - trough

listener

Let's use the superposition principle again to see what waveform he will hear:

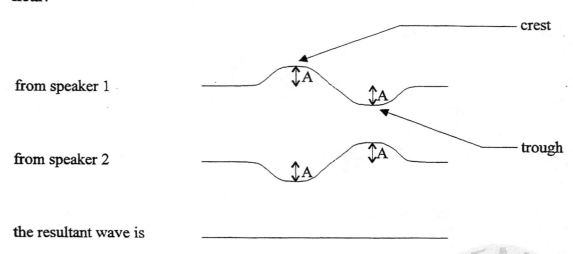

from speaker 1

from speaker 2

the resultant wave is _____

The waves cancel out completely. He will hear nothing at all! This is destructive interference, and the waves are **out of phase**.

Destructive interference happens when two waves are out of phase: they always meet crest-to-trough, and completely cancel each other.

We can find the points where there will be constructive and destructive interference by knowing the wavelength of the interfering waves. In fact, the listener doesn't have to always sit at equal distances from the speakers to hear the constructive interference. He just has to sit so that the *difference* in the distances is equal to a whole number (1, 2, 3, etc.) of wavelengths. If the difference in the distances is a *half*-whole number (1 1/2, 2 1/2, etc.), there will be destructive interference. The next example should help show this.

Example: Will wants to listen to his stereo, and the wavelength of the tone he's playing is 1 m. Does he hear a loud tone, or no tone at all when he's sitting:
(a) 1 m from one speaker and 2 m from the other ?

The wavelength of the tone is 1 m, so if the difference between the distances to the speakers is a whole number of wavelengths (1 m, 2 m, 3 m, etc.), there is constructive interference. If the distance is a half-whole number of wavelengths (.5 m, 1.5 m, 2.5 m, etc.), there is destructive interference.

The difference between the distances from the speakers is

$$2 \text{ m} - 1 \text{ m} = 1 \text{ m}$$

This is a whole number of wavelengths, so **he hears constructive interference, and a loud tone**.

(b) 1.5 m from one speaker and 4 m from the other ?

The difference between the distances from the speakers is

$$4 \text{ m} - 1.5 \text{ m} = 2.5 \text{ m}$$

This is a half number of wavelengths, so **he hears destructive interference, and no tone**.

(c) 3.8 m from one speaker and 4.3 m from the other ?

The difference between the distances from the speakers is

$$4.3 \text{ m} - 3.8 \text{ m} = 0.5 \text{ m}$$

This is a half number of wavelengths, so **he hears destructive interference, and no tone**.

What happens when the difference in the distance is somewhere between a whole wavelength and a half-wavelength ? At these points, the listener would hear the tone at some loudness *between* the maximum and minimum volumes.

Interference happens with *all* types of waves.

Diffraction

When waves hit obstacles while they're propagating, like edges or corners, they bend around them. This is why you can hear your stereo even if you leave the room. If the waves didn't bend, you would be able to hear anything that wasn't coming at you in a direct line. This bending of waves around things is called **diffraction**.

We're going to look at diffraction through a single slit. When we send straight waves through a thin slit, we get a **diffraction pattern**, caused by wave interference. The diffraction pattern we see is a semi-circular pattern of maxima (where waves meet crest-to-crest or trough-to-trough), and minima (where the crests and troughs cancel each other).

Single-slit Diffraction

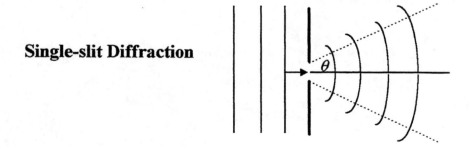

The wave shows constructive interference (a maximum) between the dashed lines in the picture above. If you go past either of these lines, you will hit a minimum (destructive interference), and then another very weak maximum. The size of the region of the central maximum depends on the wavelength and the width of the slit (D). If the angle between the centre line, and either of the dashed lines is θ, then this relation gives the size of the angle of the constructive interference:

$$\sin \theta = \frac{\lambda}{D}$$

Transverse Standing Waves

Water waves, sound waves, and pulses on strings or Slinkys are traveling waves, because they move from one place to another. A **standing wave** is a wave that stays in one place, like a vibrating guitar string. They are caused by two identical traveling waves that are going in opposite directions. *A standing wave is the resultant wave of two identical, oppositely traveling waves that combine according to the principle of superposition.*

Here are three standing waves:

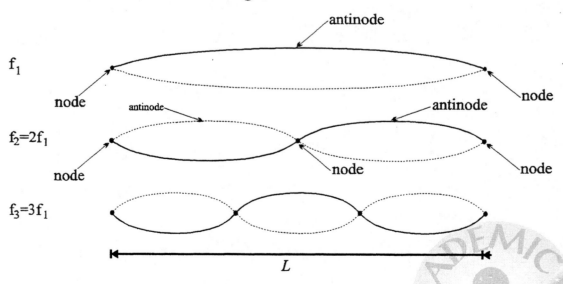

Any standing wave has nodes and anti-nodes. A **node** is a point on the standing wave where there is no vibration at all. An **anti-node** is a point where there is maximum vibration.

Each standing wave has a specific frequency of vibration. The first drawing above is the fundamental frequency, call it f_1. This is lowest possible frequency at which that particular string can vibrate, and there's only one loop. All the other standing wave frequencies for that particular string are multiples of this fundamental frequency, called **harmonics**. The second drawing is the second harmonic, f_2, equal to $2f_1$. The last drawing is the third harmonic, $f_3 = 3f_1$. The **harmonic number** (the subscript on the f) is equal to the number of loops, or anti-nodes. In general, we can say:

The **nth harmonic of a standing wave** is

$$f_n = nf_1,$$

where f_1 is the first harmonic (fundamental frequency), and n is also equal to the number of anti-nodes.

If we find the first harmonic at 10 Hz, the second will be at 20 Hz, the third will be at 30 Hz, etc.

A standing wave is actually resonance effect. The first harmonic is also the natural frequency of the string. Unlike springs and pendulums, strings can resonate at many different frequencies.

We can predict the frequency of the harmonics. Suppose we say the length of our string is L. Looking at the diagrams, we see that each loop is actually a half a wavelength. A whole number of loops, or half-wavelengths, fits on the standing wave, or

$$L = n\left(\frac{1}{2}\lambda_n\right),$$

where n is the number of half-wavelengths (or loops, or anti-nodes).

so $\qquad \lambda_n = \dfrac{2L}{n}$

and use $\quad \lambda_n = \dfrac{v}{f_n}$ (*v* is the speed of the wave) to get

$$\frac{2L}{n} = \frac{v}{f_n}$$

and rearrange this to find a the relation for **the harmonic frequencies for a string held at both ends**:

$$\boxed{f_n = n\left(\frac{v}{2L}\right)}$$

where *v* is the speed of the wave, *L* is the length of the string, and n is the harmonic number (n = 1, 2, 3, 4,...).

Longitudinal Standing Waves

Sound waves are longitudinal waves. When you play a musical wind instrument, what you're really doing is setting up standing waves in the instrument's tube.

This is a bit different than the standing wave on a string, because the ends of the tube can be open or closed. This will change the shape of the standing wave.

Both ends open: If both ends of the tube are open, the first three harmonics look like this:

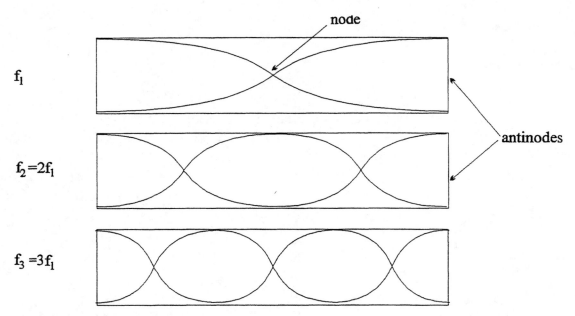

Unlike the string, there are *anti-nodes* on the ends of the standing waves. We can determine the frequencies of the harmonics the exact same way as we did with the string.

The harmonic frequencies for a tube open at both ends:

$$f_n = n\left(\frac{v}{2L}\right)$$

where v is the speed of the wave, L is the length of the string, and n is the harmonic number (n = 1, 2, 3, 4,...).

One end open, the other end closed: If only one end of the tube is open, the first three harmonics look like this:

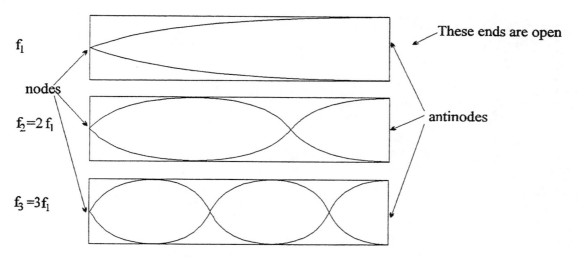

This time, there's an anti-nodes at the open end, and a node at the closed end. We can determine the frequencies of the harmonics in a similar way that we did in the other two cases, but remember that here, the first harmonic is a *quarter* wavelength, not a half. Looking at the picture above, it is also obvious that *there can only ever be an odd number of quarter wavelengths, so only odd numbered harmonics exist.*

The harmonic frequencies for a tube open at one end:

$$f_n = n\left(\frac{v}{4L}\right)$$

where v is the speed of the wave, L is the length of the string, and n is the harmonic number (n = 1, 3, 5,...).

Since the closed ended tube has a factor of 1/4 where the open ended tube has a factor of 1/2, we see that a tube with two open ends must have twice the length of a tube with one open end to get the same fundamental frequency. Musical wind instruments like the flute are really tubes open at both ends.

Example: *Robin usually practices her piccolo at room temperature, when the speed of sound is 343 m/s. One day, she is playing outside in cold weather, and the speed of sound in the air is 335 m/s. If her piccolo is 25 cm long from the mouth piece to the end, and is open at both ends, by how much does the fundamental frequency ?*

We need to find the fundamental frequencies at room, and outdoor temperatures. At the fundamental frequency, n =1, and

$$25 \text{ cm} = 25 \times 10^{-2} \text{ m} = 0.25 \text{ m.}$$

$$f_n = n\left(\frac{v}{2L}\right)$$

at room temp.:
$$f_1 = 1\left(\frac{343 \text{ m/s}}{2(0.25 \text{ m})}\right) = 686 \text{ Hz}$$

outside:
$$f_1 = 1\left(\frac{335 \text{ m/s}}{2(0.25 \text{ m})}\right) = 670 \text{ Hz}$$

The difference in frequency is 686 Hz - 670 Hz **= 16 Hz**.

Wind instruments have a join at the mouthpiece, so that the musician can change the length of the tube. This means Robin can correct for the cold temperature, so she doesn't have to play out of tune while she's outside.

PHYSICS GRADE 11

Mechanical Waves Practice Problems

1. Draw a waveform, and indicate the period, wavelength, amplitude, and undisturbed position.

2. (a) From the following waveform (and using a ruler), find the frequency and wavelength of the wave.

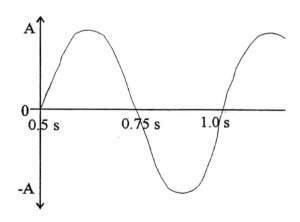

(b) Find the wavespeed of the wave.

PHYSICS GRADE 11

3. You're on a train moving at 45 m/s toward a stationary whistle sounding. The whistle sounds at 300 Hz. The speed of sound is 343 m/s.

(a) What frequency do you hear as the trains approaches ? What frequency do you hear as the train moves away ?

(b) What's the Doppler shift in each case ?

PHYSICS GRADE 11

4. Sketch the resultant wave of these square pulses when they're superimposed. The pulses all have the same wavelength.

(a)

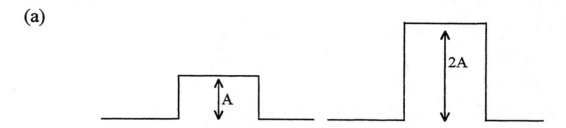

(b)

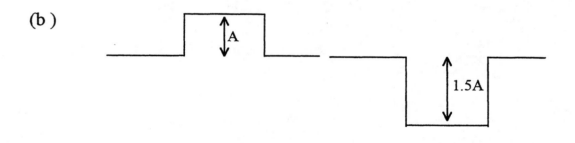

(c)

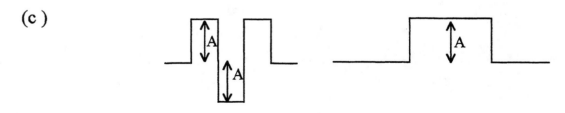

5. Neil sits in front of a pair of speakers, which are playing one note. Where he's sitting, he can't hear any noise at all. If one speaker is turned off, what will he hear ?

6. Darren stands 3.0 m in front of a door (0.75 m wide) which leads to a room with a playing stereo. He finds that when he moves 2.0 m to the right, like in the picture below, the sound begins to drop off suddenly. Using single-slit diffraction theory, what's the wavelength of the sound waves ?

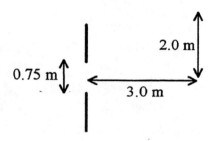

PHYSICS GRADE 11

7. A string has a fundamental frequency of 50 Hz.
(a) If a higher harmonic standing wave has 6 nodes, what's the frequency ?

(b) If the speed of the wave is 20 m/s, what's the length of the string ?

(c) If the same fundamental frequency were produced by a longitudinal standing wave in a tube with one open end, what would be the tube length (speed of sound = 343 m/s) ?

PHYSICS GRADE 11

Mechanical Waves Practice Problem Solutions

1. Draw a waveform, and indicate the period, wavelength, amplitude, and undisturbed position.

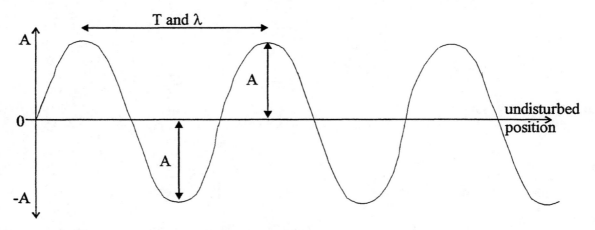

2. (a) From the following waveform (and using a ruler), find the frequency and wavelength of the wave.

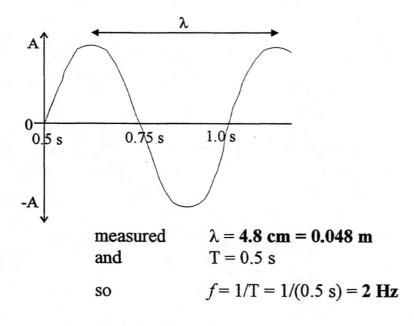

measured λ = **4.8 cm = 0.048 m**

and   T = 0.5 s

so f = 1/T = 1/(0.5 s) = **2 Hz**

(b) Find the wavespeed of the wave.

$$v = \lambda f = (0.048 \text{ m})(2 \text{ Hz}) = \textbf{0.096 m/s}$$

3. You're on a train moving at 45 m/s toward a stationary whistle sounding. The whistle sounds at 300 Hz. The speed of sound is 343 m/s.

(a) What frequency do you hear as the trains approaches ? What frequency do you hear as the train moves away ?

Approaching: $f' = f\left(1 + \dfrac{v_o}{v}\right)$

$$= (300 \text{ Hz})\left(1 + \dfrac{45 \text{ m/s}}{343 \text{ m/s}}\right) = \textbf{339 Hz}$$

Moving away: $f' = f\left(1 - \dfrac{v_o}{v}\right)$

$$= (300 \text{ Hz})\left(1 - \dfrac{45 \text{ m/s}}{343 \text{ m/s}}\right) = \textbf{261 Hz}$$

(b) What's the Doppler shift in each case ?

Approaching: the Doppler shift is

$$f' - f = 339 \text{ Hz} - 300 \text{ Hz} = \textbf{39 Hz}$$

Moving away: the Doppler shift is

$$f' - f = 261 \text{ Hz} - 300 \text{ Hz} = \textbf{-39 Hz}$$

4. *Sketch the resultant wave of these square pulses when they're superimposed. The pulses all have the same wavelength.*

(a)

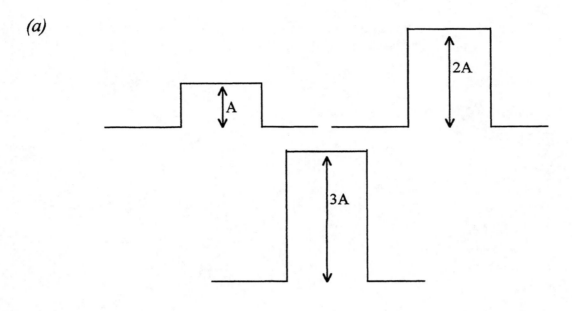

(b)

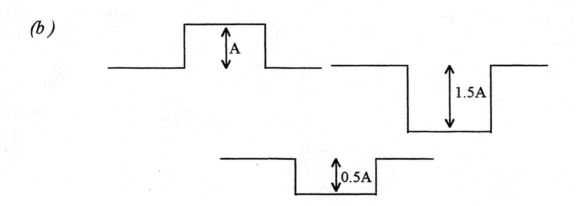

(c)

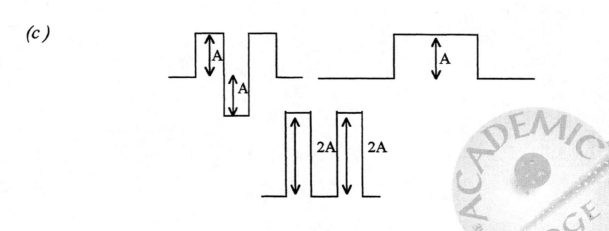

5. *Neil sits in front of a pair of speakers, which are playing one note. Where he's sitting, he can't hear any noise at all. If one speaker is turned off, what will he hear ?*

Neil will hear the note from one speaker. When both the speakers are on, he doesn't hear anything because there's destructive interference happening where he's sitting. If one speaker is turned off, there are no other waves to interefere with the waves from the speaker which is still on, so he hears the sound from one speaker.

6. *Darren stands 3.0 m in front of a door (0.75 m wide) which leads to a room with a playing stereo. He finds that when he moves 2.0 m to the right, like in the picture below, the sound begins to drop off suddenly. Using single-slit diffraction theory, what's the wavelength of the sound waves ?*

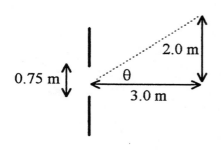

We can find the wavelength using

$$\sin\theta = \frac{\lambda}{D},$$

and find the angle with trigonometry

$$\tan\theta = \frac{2.0 \text{ m}}{3.0 \text{ m}} = 0.667$$

so $\qquad \theta = 33.7°$

Now $\qquad \lambda = D \sin\theta$

$\qquad\qquad = (0.75 \text{ m})(\sin 33.7°)$

$\qquad \lambda = \textbf{0.42 m}$

7. A string has a fundamental frequency of 50 Hz.
(a) If a higher harmonic standing wave has 6 nodes, what's the frequency ?

We use $\qquad f_n = nf_1$,

n is the harmonic number, or the number of anti-nodes. There's one fewer nodes than antinodes on a resonating string, so n = 5 here.

$$f_5 = 5 f_1 = 5 \,(50 \text{ Hz}) = \mathbf{250 \text{ Hz}}$$

(b) If the speed of the wave is 20 m/s, what's the length of the string ?

Use $\qquad f_n = n\left(\dfrac{v}{2L}\right)$, and use the fundamental frequency,

so $\qquad f_1 = \left(\dfrac{v}{2L}\right)$

$$L = \frac{v}{2f_1} = \frac{20 \text{ m/s}}{2(50 \text{ Hz})} = \mathbf{0.20 \text{ m}}$$

(c) If the same fundamental frequency were produced by a longitudinal standing wave in a tube with one open end, what would be the tube length (speed of sound = 343 m/s) ?

Use $\qquad f_n = n\left(\dfrac{v}{4L}\right)$, and use the fundamental frequency,

so $\qquad f_1 = \left(\dfrac{v}{4L}\right)$

$$L = \frac{v}{4f_1} = \frac{343 \text{ m/s}}{4(50 \text{ Hz})} = \mathbf{1.7 \text{ m}}$$

Geometric Optics

In this unit, we're going to talk about some of the properties of light; how it reflects, refracts and disperses.

Light

Light is a part of our everyday lives. We're pretty concerned to always have a source of light around. When we go in the woods, camping or hiking, we always bring flashlights and lanterns, just in case... For something so important to us, we really don't know an awful lot about it, and what we do know took a long time to figure out.

Light travels in straight lines. We can all see this just by looking at a shadow. If light diffracted going around corners, like sound waves do, the edges of the shadows would look fuzzy. They don't look fuzzy, so we say light travels in **rays** (straight lines). This is also called **linear propagation**.

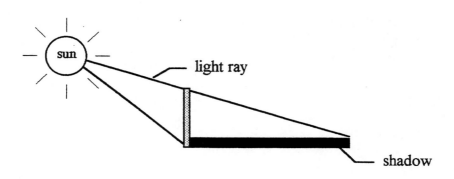

PHYSICS GRADE 11

The Speed of Light

There have been many attempts to measure the speed of light throughout history. It has always been a problem, since it's so darned *fast*! Galileo found this out when he tried to measure the speed of light with a friend one night. They both brought lanterns, and walked far apart. Galileo's friend had been told to uncover his lantern as soon as he saw Galileo's lantern, and the idea was to see how long it was from the time Galileo uncovered his lantern, to the time he saw his friend's. Of course, light travels *much* to fast for Galileo to have recorded *any* amount of time at all!

Several people tried to measure the speed of light by using astronomical methods; looking at planets and moons. The problem here is that the distances weren't known accurately enough to accurately calculate the speed.

In the 1800's Armand Fizeau developed a good method of measuring the speed of light, diagrammed below. He used a wheel with notches, and rotated it between the light source and a reflecting mirror. The light ray had to pass through a notch to get to the mirror, and through a notch in the wheel to get back (Fizeau put the mirror 8633 m away from the wheel) .

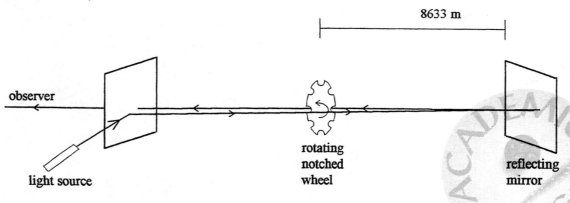

The light will only get back through a notch is the wheel is rotated at the right speed, such that the light will pass through one of the notches on the way back. If this happens, the time for the round trip of the light is the same time as it takes for the wheel to rotate to the next notch. Using this method, he found the speed of light to be 3.13×10^8 m/s.

In 1926 Albert Michelson improved Fizeau's experiment. He used a rotating octagonal mirror instead of a rotating notched wheel. Light reflects from one side of the rotating mirror, then is reflected back by *another* mirror 35 km away.

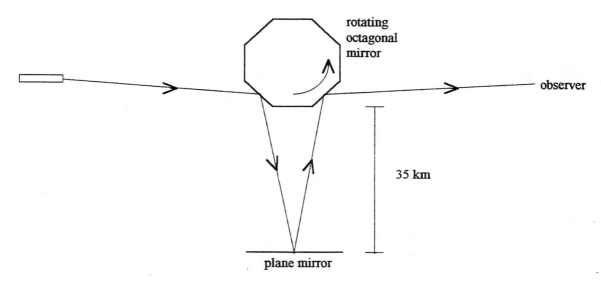

If everything is set up *just so*, the light will be reflected by the octagonal mirror *again* as it comes back, into the eye of the observer. This is a *really* tricky experiment, but Michelson got it to work, and found the speed of light to be $2.99\ 796 \times 10^8$ m/s. Since then, more accurate experiments have put the value of the speed of light at $c = 299\ 792\ 458$ m/s, so Michelson was amazingly close! We usually just use 3.00×10^8 m/s in our calculations.

PHYSICS GRADE 11

Example: *In Michelson's experiment described above, the rotational speed of the mirror was 540 revolutions/second. Calculate the speed of light.*

We know that the mirror rotates 1/8 of a revolution to the next mirror. It rotates exactly this much between the time the light beam leaves octagonal mirror, and returns to it. How long does this take?

$$540 \frac{rev}{s} \text{ which is } \frac{1}{540} \frac{s}{rev}.$$

so 1/8 of a revolution will take $\dfrac{\frac{1}{540} \frac{s}{rev}}{8}$ seconds, which is equal

to $\qquad$ 2.31 x 10^{-4} s.

The distance the light travels in this time is

2 x 35 km (for the return trip) = 70 km = 70 x 10^3 m.

Now use $v = d/t$ to find the speed of light:

$$v = \frac{d}{t} = \frac{70 \times 10^3 \text{ m}}{2.31 \times 10^{-4} \text{ s}} = \textbf{3.0 x 10}^8 \textbf{ m/s}$$

This is the speed of light.

Light rays act a lot like waves. When we talked about wave behaviour, we discussed wave reflection and refraction. We find that the same behaviour happens with light.

Reflection of Light

We see light reflection every time we look at a mirror, or a shiny surface. Most objects reflect at least a bit of the light that hits them, other, like mirrors, reflect pretty much *all* of it.

When light hits a smooth surface, it reflects at the same angle that it hit with, like this

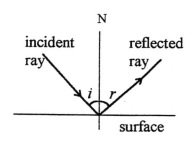

The **incident ray** is the incoming ray, and the **reflected ray** is the outgoing ray. "N" is the **normal**. The normal is a straight line drawn perpendicular to the surface. The incident ray angle (I), and the reflected ray angle (r) are measured from the normal, as shown in the drawing. This is the law of reflection of light.

The law of reflection: If the incident ray, the reflected ray, and the normal to the surface all lie in the same plane, the angle between the incident ray and the normal (**the angle of incidence**) is equal to the angle between the reflected ray and the normal (**the angle of reflection**), or
$$<i = <r$$

From the law of reflection, we see that a flat surface will have parallel reflected rays, but a curved surface won't.

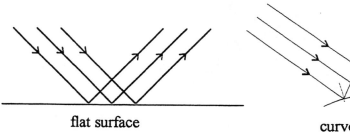

flat surface   curved surface

PHYSICS GRADE 11

We can find the direction of a reflected rays on a curved surface at any point by drawing a tangent to the point, like in the picture below. We can then draw a normal line to the tangent, and use the law of reflection to find the direction of the reflected ray.

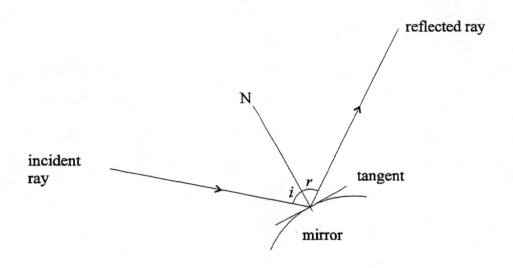

Example: *Two reflecting surfaces put so there's an angle of 75° between them. A light ray hit the first surface at an angle of 45° to the normal line. What will be the angle of reflection of the second surface.*

This can be done geometrically. First we draw incident and reflected rays from the first mirror, and add in the angles and the normal lines. We know from the law of reflection that the reflected ray from the first mirror has to be at an angle of 45° to the normal.

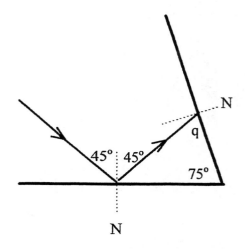

We know that the angle between the normal line and the surface is 90°, so the angle between the reflected ray and the surface has to be

$$90° - 45° = 45°.$$

We also know that the sum of the angles of any triangle is 180°. We'll use this on the corner triangle to find out the angle of "q".

$$q + 45° + 75° = 180°$$

so $\qquad q = 180° - 45° - 75° = 60°$

so the incident ray on the second surface has to be 90° - 60° = 30°.

Using the law of reflection again, we know that if the angle of incidence on the second surface is 30°, the angle of **reflection will also be 30°**.

Let's redraw the triangle with all these angles,

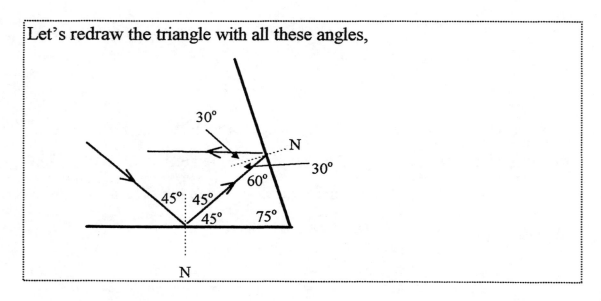

The Index of Refraction and Refraction of Light

When we looked at pulses on strings hitting boundaries, we saw that sometimes a pulse was completely reflected, and sometimes it was completely transmitted, and sometimes it was partially reflected and partially transmitted. The same things can happen with light rays. When light strikes a mirror, it is totally reflected. When light hits the mirrored side of a one-way mirror (a mirror that looks like glass on one side and a mirror on the other), it is partially reflected, and partially transmitted. When light hits glass, is often completely transmitted.

We noticed the pulse on the string changed a bit when it crossed a boundary. Light rays change a bit too; they change their angle to the normal. This is called **refraction**. *Light changes its direction as it passes from one medium to another, if the light doesn't hit the surface parallel to the normal.* Light that hits a surface parallel to the normal will go straight through, with no deflection.

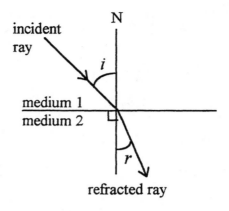

How much does it change its direction ? That depends on the medium, and its **index of refraction** An index of refraction is a measure of how fast light travels through a medium (the speed of light changes slightly from medium to medium. The value of c we usually use is for a vacuum).

> **The index of refraction** (n) is the ratio of the speed of light in a vacuum (c) to the speed of light in the medium (v), or
> $$n = c/v$$

Here are the index of refraction values for some common substances:

Substance	Index of Refraction
diamond	2.419
glass	1.52
ice	1.309
water	1.33
air	1.000 293

How do we know how much refraction happens ? We can find the angle of refraction using Snell's law of refraction.

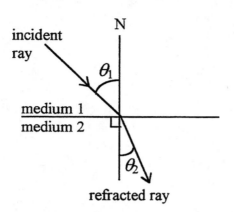

incident ray

N

θ_1

medium 1
medium 2

θ_2

refracted ray

Snell's law of refraction: The angle of incidence in medium 1 is θ_1, and the index of refraction in medium 1 is n_1, and the angle of incidence in medium 2 is θ_2, and the index of refraction is n_2. The relation between these variables is

$$n_1 \sin\theta_1 = n_2 \sin\theta_2$$

Can we predict whether the refracted ray will bend toward the normal, or away from the normal ? Yes, actually, we can. If light moves from a medium of lower index of refraction to one of higher index of refraction, the refracted ray is bent *toward* the normal.

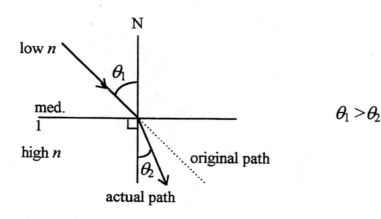

N

low n

θ_1

med. 1

high n

θ_2

original path

actual path

$\theta_1 > \theta_2$

If it goes from a region of higher index of refraction to lower index of refraction, then the refracted ray is bent *away* from the normal.

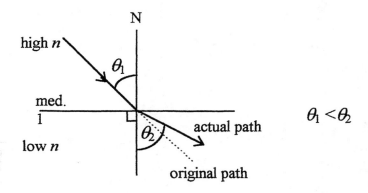

The next example uses Snell's law.

Example: *A light beam passes into a pool of still of water from a 60°
angle with the surface of the water. What is the angle of refraction ?
Does the refracted ray bend toward, or away from the normal ?*

We can use Snell's law to find the angle of refraction. We first need to

find the angle on incidence.

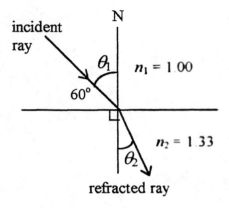

We know the total angle

between the normal and the

surface is 90°, so

$$\theta_1 + 60° = 90°$$

so $\quad \theta_1 = 90° - 60° = 30°$

We know that the index of refraction for air is about 1.00, and the index of

refraction for water is 1.33, so $n_1 = 1$, and $n_2 = 1.33$. Now

$$n_1 \sin\theta_1 = n_2 \sin\theta_2$$

so $\quad\quad \sin\theta_2 = \dfrac{n_1 \sin\theta_1}{n_2}$

$$= \dfrac{1.00 \sin 30°}{1.33}$$

$$= 0.376$$

and so $\quad\quad \theta_2 = 22°$

The angle of refraction is 22°, so **the ray bends toward the normal**.

The same rules can be used for curved surfaces. It just gets a bit trickier, since the refracted rays aren't all going in the same direction anymore. Like before, we can draw a tangent to the surface, and a normal to the tangent line. Then we can apply all the same laws as we would to a plane surface.

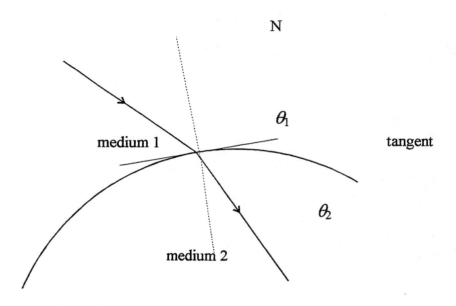

Total Internal Reflection

When light passes from a medium with a higher index or refraction like glass, to one of a lower index of refraction, like air, the angle of refraction is larger than the angle of incidence. As the angle of incidence gets larger, the angle of refraction gets larger. If we keep making the angle of incidence larger, it will eventually reach a certain value, called the **critical value** (θ_c), where the angle of refraction is $90°$. If the angle of refraction is $90°$, the refracted ray points along the medium boundary, like in the second drawing below.

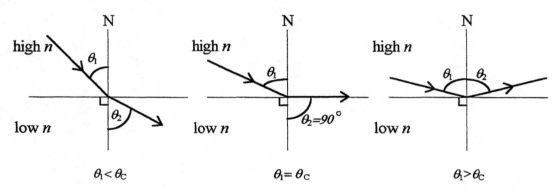

The third drawing shows what happens if we keep increasing the angle of incidence. All the incident light gets *reflected* back. This is called **total internal reflection**. Total internal reflection can only happen if the light is going from a high index of refraction to a lower index of refraction.

We can predict the critical angle of any boundary using Snell's law:

$$n_1 \sin\theta_1 = n_2 \sin\theta_2$$

The critical angle is when $\theta_1 = \theta_c$, and $\theta_2 = 90°$.

so
$$n_1 \sin\theta_c = n_2 \sin 90°$$

or
$$\sin\theta_c = \frac{n_2 \sin 90°}{n_1}$$

so
$$\sin\theta_c = \frac{n_2}{n_1}$$

> The **critical angle** is the angle where total internal reflection begins to happen, and is given by
> $$\sin\theta_c = n_2 / n_1$$

Example: *What is the critical angle for light passing from water into air ?*

We know that the index of refraction for air is about 1.00, and the index of refraction for water is 1.33, so $n_1 = 1.33$, and $n_2 = 1$, so

$$\sin\theta_c = \frac{n_2}{n_1} = \frac{1}{1.33} = 0.752$$

$$\theta_c = 49°$$

If the incident ray hits at an angle greater than 49°, total internal reflection will happen.

This is how fiber optics work. Fiber optic cables are being used in medicine, and many communications systems. The waves in the fibers are total internally reflected time after time, all the way down the fiber.

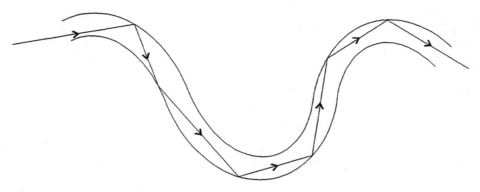

Dispersion of Light: Prisms

If we send a ray of white light through a prism we a pattern of colours that looks like a rainbow. This is an example of light **dispersion**.

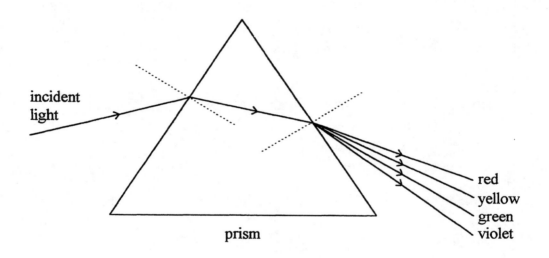

incident
light

red
yellow
green
violet

prism

Now, what exactly is happening to make this pattern of colours ? We talked about how the speed of a light ray depends on it's medium, but the *speed depends on the wavelength of the light*, just like it does for mechanical waves. This means that *rays of light with different wavelengths, or frequencies, will refract different amounts at a medium boundary*. White light (like light from the sun) is actually all colours of light put together. This table lists the wavelengths of the different colours.

PHYSICS GRADE 11

Wavelengths of Different Colours of Light

Colour	Wavelength (in 10^{-9} m)
red	660
orange	610
yellow	580
green	550
blue	470
violet	410

When the while light passes through the prism, it gets **dispersed** into its colours, since each colour has a different wavelength. The colours will always appear in the same order, since they are always refracted the same amount. This is why the colour order in rainbows is always the same. Rainbows are caused by the dispersion of sunlight through raindrops in the air, much like the dispersion that happens in a prism.

Plane Mirrors

Mirrors can be very useful things, like the ones in your house, or the one your dentist uses to look at your teeth. These mirrors give an exact image of what you, or your teeth, look like. Mirrors are sometimes designed to give distorted images, like fun-house mirrors, or concave make-up mirrors that *really* magnify those pores. The first type of mirror is usually a flat, or plane mirror. The second type is curved. We can look at how light reflects from either type using the law of reflection $(<i = <r)$.

The first type of mirror mentioned is a plane mirror. When you look at the image of yourself in a plane mirror, you'll notice four things:

    1- your image is upright

    2- it's the same size as you

    3- the image looks as far behind the mirror as you are in front of it

    4- left and right are reversed (if you raise your left hand, the image raised its right hand. This is why letters look backward in a mirror).

This diagram should help you see why it's like this.

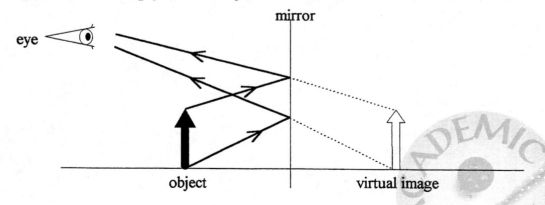

Light from the object hits the mirror, and is reflected into your eye. Your eye "knows" that light travels in straight lines, so it interprets the light as coming from behind the mirror, like in the diagram above. The dashed line is the *apparent* (not true) path of the light ray. The image your eye sees is called a **virtual image**, since the light rays don't actually come from the image.

We can use some geometry to show that the distance from the real object to the mirror is the same as the apparent distance from the virtual image to the mirror.

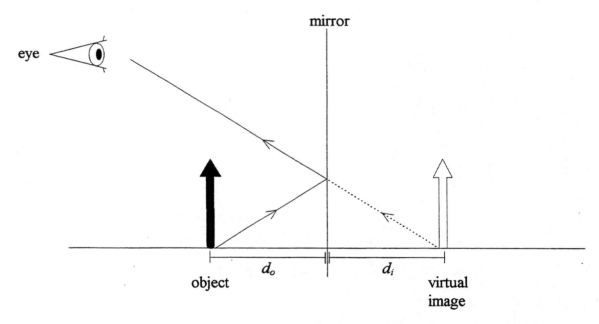

The diagram shows that the angles in both triangles are the same, and the two triangle share a side (at the mirror), so the triangles are identical. Since they're the same the lengths of the bottom sides are the same (d_o and d_i), so the distance of the image to the mirror (d_i) is the same as the distance of the object the mirror (d_o).

Curved mirrors

Curved mirrors are usually **spherical** mirrors; mirrors that are shaped like a section of a sphere. They can be **concave**, or **convex**, as in the drawings below.

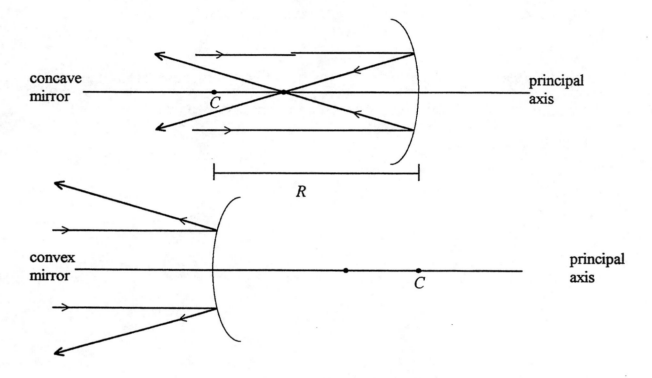

For both a concave and convex lenses, there's a point called the **centre of curvature**, C, located at the **radius of curvature**, R. The radius of curvature is where the centre of the sphere would be, had we not cut the mirror out of the sphere. The **principal axis** is a line that goes through the centre of curvature and the centre of the mirror.

Light from an object hits the mirror, and the rays are reflected so that they all converge at one point. This is the **image point**, and is where the image is formed. If the object being reflected in a mirror is very far away, so that the light rays hitting the mirror from the object are all parallel, all the light rays will converge at one spot (or at least look like they converge at the same spot, in the case of the convex mirror).

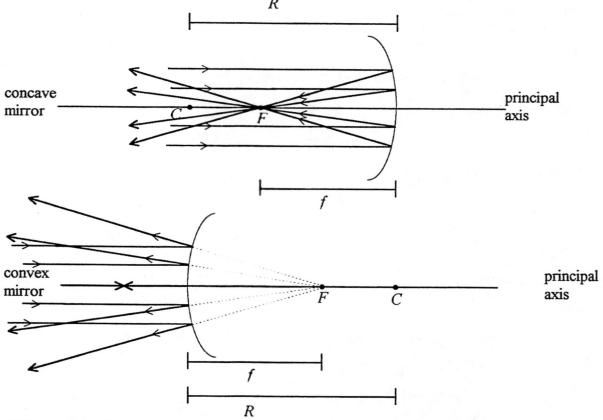

The point where the rays converge, and where the image of the object will be formed, is called the **focal point**, F. The focal point is a distance called the **focal length**, f, away from the mirror. The focal point is located halfway between the center of curvature and the mirror, or

focal length of a concave mirror: $f = \dfrac{1}{2}R$

focal length of a convex mirror: $f = -\dfrac{1}{2}R$

The focal length is negative for a convex mirror, because the focal point is behind the mirror.

We can see from the pictures above that concave mirrors have **real images**, because the light rays *actually* come from the image point. The convex mirror has a **virtual image**, since it just *looks* like the rays are coming from behind the mirror.

Now we're going to look at how these types of mirrors form images.

Concave mirrors: We can find the position, and size of an image of an object by looking at only three rays of light coming from the top of the object.

1- a ray from the top of the object going to the mirror parallel to the principal axis. This ray is reflected through the focal point of the mirror (the solid line in the diagram below).

2- a ray from the top of the object, then through the focal point, before being reflected by the mirror. The reflected ray will be parallel to the principal axis (the dashed line).

3- a ray that goes from the centre of curvature, then to the object. This ray hits the mirror perpendicular to the mirror's surface, so the ray is reflected straight back (the dotted line).

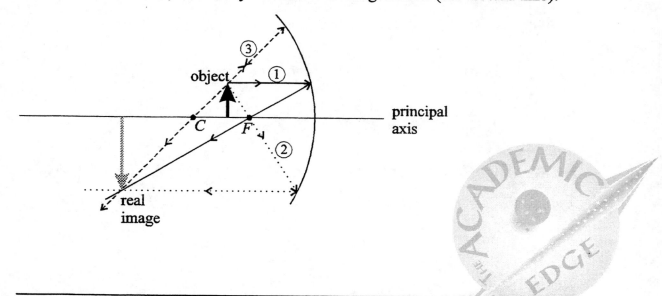

We can see from this diagram that *if the object is placed between the centre of curvature and the focal point of the concave mirror, the image is real, bigger and inverted.*

What if we put the object beyond the centre of curvature ? We can use the same rays to get this diagram. The only difference this time is that the direction of the rays is *reversed*. We know that rays will follow the same straight line going in either direction. This is the **principle of reversibility**. The ray diagram we get this time is this one:

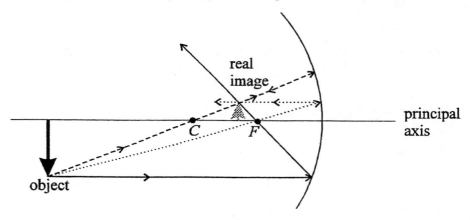

We see that *if the object is placed beyond the centre of curvature of the concave mirror, the image is real, smaller, and inverted.*

What if the object is placed between the focal point and the mirror ? We'll again draw a ray diagram with the same three rays.

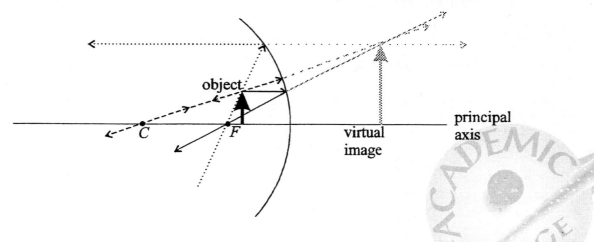

We get a virtual image this time. *If the object is placed between the focal point and the concave mirror, the image is virtual, upright, and enlarged.* This is how those enlarging make-up mirrors work.

Convex mirrors: We can find the image produced by a convex mirror the same way as we did for a concave mirror, using the same rays. Remember that the focal point of the convex mirror is *behind* the mirror, so we have to extend the rays in a straight line to the focal point, like in the diagram below.

> 1- a ray from the top of the object going to the mirror parallel to the principal axis. This ray is reflected up, and if it's traced back, it looks like it's coming from the focal point of the mirror (the solid line in the diagram below).
>
> 2- a ray from the top of the object, then straight through the mirror to the focal point. The reflected ray will be parallel to the principal axis (the dashed line).
>
> 3- a ray that goes toward the centre of curvature, then to the object. This ray hits the mirror perpendicular to the mirror's surface, so the ray is reflected straight back (the dotted line).

The ray diagram on the following page shows the three rays and the image for an object in front of the mirror.

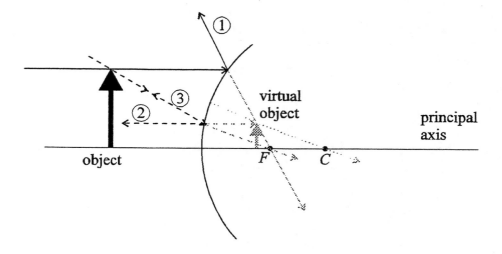

The image produced by a convex mirror is virtual, upright, and smaller than the object. Convex mirrors are the ones stores hang in upper corners as security mirrors, since they let you see a large area in a small mirror.

Curved Mirror Magnification and the Mirror Equation

We can get an idea of the size of the image using ray diagrams, but this isn't always the easiest way, particularly if you're dealing with large distances. We can take data using different mirrors, and analyze it, we would find that

$$\frac{h_i}{h_o} = \frac{d_i}{d_o} \quad \text{and} \quad \frac{h_i}{h_o} = \frac{d_o - f}{f}$$

where: h_i is the height of the image.

h_o is the height of the object.

d_i is the distance from the image to the mirror.

d_o is the distance from the object to the mirror.

f is the focal length.

We can combine these equations to get the **mirror equation**:

$$\boxed{\frac{1}{d_o} + \frac{1}{d_i} = \frac{1}{f}}$$

Magnification, m, is the size of the image, relative to the size of the object, or

$$\boxed{m = \frac{h_i}{h_o} = -\frac{d_i}{d_o}}.$$

The d_i/d_o is negative because the image is inverted for a concave mirror, and the d_i is negative for a convex mirror (the two negatives multiply together to get a positive, so an upright, image). This is just a sign convention.

A magnification value smaller than 1 *and* bigger than -1 ($-1 < m < 1$) means the image is smaller than the object. If the magnification is bigger than 1 *or* smaller than -1 ($-1 > m$ or $1 < m$), the image is bigger than the object.

We have to be very careful of signs when we use these equations! Here's a summary of what the symbols mean when they are positive and negative.

d_o: The distance from the object to the mirror

> positive if the object is in front of the mirror (real object)
> negative if the object is behind the mirror (virtual object)

d_i: The distance from the image to the mirror

> positive if the image is in front of the mirror (real image)
> negative if the image is behind the mirror (virtual image)

f: The focal length

> positive if f is in front of the mirror (concave mirror)
> negative if f is behind the mirror (convex mirror)

m: The magnification

> positive if the image is upright
> negative if the image is inverted

Some other symbols to remember are

> F: The focal point.
>
> C: The centre of curvature.
>
> R: The radius of curvature, equal to the distance between the mirror and the centre of curvature, C. $R = 2f$

Example: *An elf is stands 10 cm from a concave mirror with a focal length of 6 cm. Where is his image ? Is it real or virtual ? Is it upright or inverted ? What is the magnification ?*

We start with a ray diagram. We know that the focal length of a concave mirror is $f = \frac{1}{2}R$, so the radius of curvature (R) of the mirror is twice the focal length, or 12 cm, and the centre of curvature (C) is 12 cm in front of the mirror.

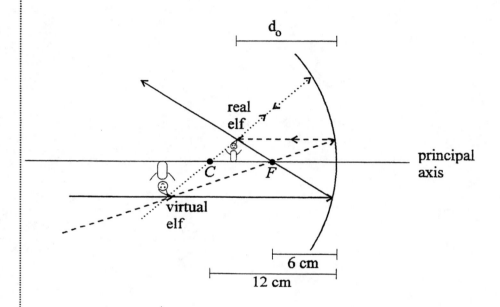

The object is placed between C and F (the focal point), so we already know the image will be **real**, and **inverted**.

We can use the mirror equation to find the image distance. Remember that the focal length, f, and the object distance, d_i, are both positive, since they are in front of the mirror.

$$\frac{1}{d_o} + \frac{1}{d_i} = \frac{1}{f}$$

so
$$\frac{1}{d_i} = \frac{1}{f} - \frac{1}{d_o} = \frac{1}{6\,cm} - \frac{1}{10\,cm} = 0.067\ 1/cm$$

and so
$$d_i = \frac{1}{0.067\ \frac{1}{cm}} = \textbf{15 cm}$$

The positive d_i means that the image is in front of the mirror, just like in the ray diagram.

The magnification can be found using

$$m = -\frac{d_i}{d_o} = -\frac{15\ cm}{10\ cm} = \textbf{-1.5 times}$$

the negative magnification means that the image is inverted, like in the ray diagram. The m value is smaller than -1, so the image is bigger than the object.

The elf sees an image of himself that is real, enlarged and inverted (magnification of -1.5 times), and located 15 cm in front of the mirror.

Example: *The same elf now stands the same distance (10 cm) in front of a convex mirror with a focal length of -6 cm. Now where is his image ? Is it real or virtual ? Is it upright or inverted ? What is the magnification ?*

We start again with a ray diagram. We know that the focal length of a convex mirror is $f = -\frac{1}{2}R$, so the radius of curvature (R) of the mirror is the twice the focal length, or 12 cm, and the centre of curvature (C) is 12 cm *behind* the convex mirror.

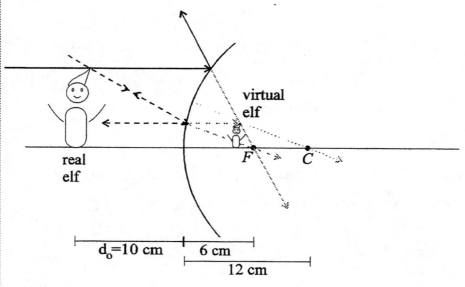

When we are working with a convex mirror the image will always be **virtual**, and **upright**.

We can again use the mirror equation to find the image distance. Remember that the focal length, f, is negative, since it's behind the mirror , and the object distance, d_i, is positive.

$$\frac{1}{d_o} + \frac{1}{d_i} = \frac{1}{f}$$

so

$$\frac{1}{d_i} = \frac{1}{f} - \frac{1}{d_o} = \frac{1}{-6 \text{ cm}} - \frac{1}{10 \text{ cm}} = -0.267 \text{ 1/cm}$$

and so $\qquad d_i = \dfrac{1}{-0.267\ \dfrac{1}{cm}} = $ **-3.8 cm**

The negative d_i means that the image is behind the mirror, just like in the ray diagram.

The magnification can be found using

$$m = -\dfrac{d_i}{d_o} = -\dfrac{-3.8\ cm}{10\ cm} = 0.38 \text{ times}$$

the positive magnification means that the image is upright, like in the ray diagram. The m value is smaller than 1, and bigger than -1, so the image is smaller than the object.

The elf sees an image of himself that is virtual, smaller and upright (magnification of 0.38 times), and located 3.8 cm in front of the mirror.

Lenses

We use lenses *all* the time. Glasses, contact lenses, telescopes, magnifying glasses, and cameras all just a very few examples of the places where we see them. Knowing how light reflects from mirrors gives us a starting point to discuss how lenses refract light.

There are two basic kinds of lenses, converging and diverging. Ad their names might tell you, a converging lens makes light rays converge to a point, and a diverging lens spreads the light rays out, like in the diagram below.

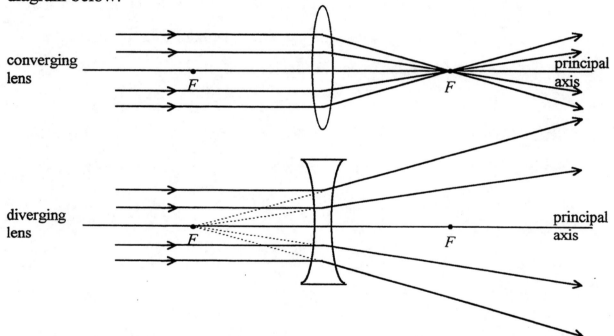

You can see the big difference between lenses and mirrors is that lenses let the light through, where mirrors reflect the light. Lenses have **focal points**, *F*, like mirrors do. Actually, lenses have two focal points, one on each side of the lens. It doesn't matter which way you look through a concave or convex lens, you'll see the same image. Every lens also has a **principal axis**.

Like with mirror, we draw ray diagrams to analyze lenses.

Converging lenses: The first thing the remember is to put a focal point on *each side* of the lens on the principal axis (they're the same distance from the lens on each side), like in the diagram below. Then we draw in three rays (We actually only need two rays to locate the image, but it's good to draw the third as a check.):

> 1- a ray that is parallel to the principal axis. When it goes through the lens, it will be refracted such it goes through the focal point on the other side (solid line).

> 2- a ray that goes through the focal point be fore hitting the lens. This ray will be refracted so that it's parallel to the principal axis on the other side (dashed line).

> 3- a ray the goes through the principal axis at the centre of the lens. This ray won't be refracted (dotted line).

Where these three rays meet is the **image**.

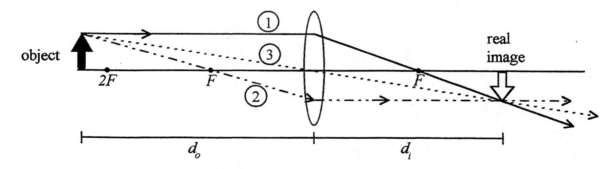

This diagram is the case where *the object is past a point twice as far away as the focal point, 2F. When this is the case, the image is real, smaller, and inverted.* This is the case in a camera.

If we move the object so that it's between *F* and 2*F*, we get this ray diagram

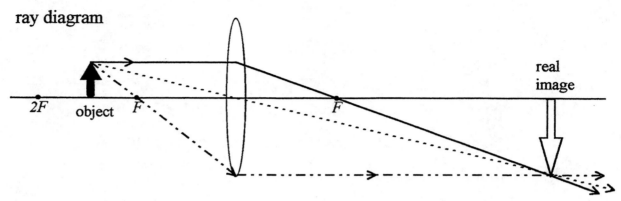

If the object is placed between a focal point, F, and a point twice as far away as the focal point, 2F, the image is real, larger, and inverted. This is what going on in a slide projector.

If we move the object so that it's between the focal point, *F*, and the lens, we find this that the rays diverge, like this,

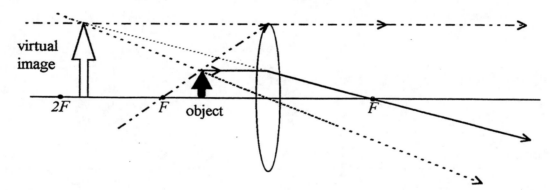

If the object is placed between the focal point and the converging lens, the image will be virtual, on the same side of the lens as the object, upright and bigger. A magnifying glass works this way.

Diverging lens: Diverging lenses are easier, since it doesn't matter where you place the object, you'll always get the same kind of image, as below. *An important thing to remember is that the focal length is negative for a diverging lens* (this is so the lens equation we're going to talk about in a bit works).

We again draw three rays.

> 1- a ray that's parallel to the principal axis until it hit the lens. When it goes through the lens, it will be refracted such that you could trace the refracted ray back to the focal point (solid line).

> 2- a ray that would go through the focal point on the *other* side of the lens if it weren't deflected. This ray will be deflected so that it's parallel to the principal axis on the other side of the lens (dashed line).

> 3- a ray the goes through the principal axis at the centre of the lens. This ray won't be refracted (dotted line).

These three rays can be traced back to the point where the **image** is located.

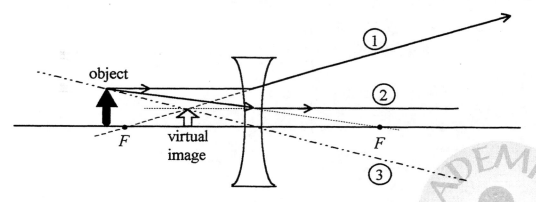

A diverging lens results in an upright, virtual image that is smaller than the object.

The Thin-Lens Equation and Magnification

Just like with mirrors, we can use an equation to help find the location of the image of a lens. In fact, we use the *same* equation, but we call it the **thin lens equation**:

$$\frac{1}{d_o} + \frac{1}{d_i} = \frac{1}{f}$$

Magnification, *m*, is also the same as it was for mirrors:

$$m = -\frac{d_i}{d_o} \quad \text{or} \quad m = \frac{h_i}{h_o}$$

A magnification value smaller than 1 *and* bigger than -1 ($-1 < m < 1$) means the image is smaller than the object. If the magnification is bigger than 1 *or* smaller than -1 ($-1 > m$ or $1 < m$), the image is bigger than the object.

When we work with lenses, we usually put the object on the left side, and always use the following sign conventions. Here's a summary of what the symbols mean when they are positive and negative.

d_o: The distance from the object to the lens

> positive if the object is to the left of the lens (real object)
> negative if the object is to the right of the lens (virtual object)

d_i: The distance from the image to the lens

> positive if the image is real, and to the right of the lens.
> negative if the image is virtual, and to the left of the lens.

f: The focal length

> positive for a converging lens
> negative for a diverging lens

m: The magnification

> positive if the image is upright
> negative if the image is inverted

Example: *A camera's (real) image is located 2 cm from the lens. If the object is 15 cm in front of the camera lens, what is the focal length of the lens? What is the size of the image, if the object is 40 cm high?*

We first draw a diagram. We know that if the image is real, it has to be to the right of the lens.

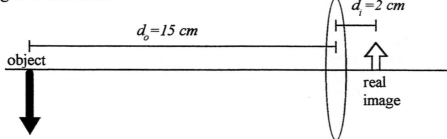

We can use the thin lens equation to find the focal length.

$$\frac{1}{f} = \frac{1}{d_o} + \frac{1}{d_i}$$

Remember the sign conventions! d_o *is positive, and so is* d_i.

$$\frac{1}{f} = \frac{1}{15 \text{ cm}} + \frac{1}{2 \text{ cm}} = 0.567 \text{ 1/cm}$$

so $f = 1.8$ **cm**

We can find the height of the image using $m = \frac{h_i}{h_o}$ if we find the

magnification: $m = -\frac{d_i}{d_o} = -\frac{2 \text{ cm}}{15 \text{ cm}} = -0.13$ times

so the image height is $h_i = mh_o = (-0.13)(40 \text{ cm}) = -5.2$ **cm**

The negative sign means it's inverted, as we expected.

Example: *Dawn stands 1 m in front of a diverging lens of focal length -10 cm. If Dawn is 1.73 m tall, how tall will her image be, and where will it be located?*

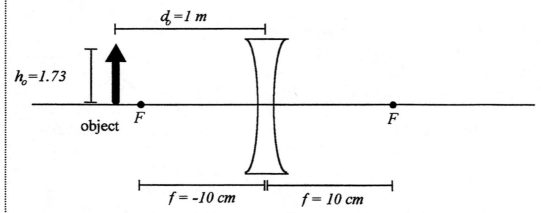

We'll use the thin lens equation to find the image location, since we know d_o and f (remember $f = -10$ cm $= -0.10$ m).

$$\frac{1}{f} = \frac{1}{d_o} + \frac{1}{d_i}$$

so

$$\frac{1}{d_i} = \frac{1}{f} - \frac{1}{d_o} = \frac{1}{-0.10 \text{ m}} - \frac{1}{1 \text{ m}} = -11 \text{ 1/m}$$

$d_i = -0.091$ **m** negative means a **virtual** image.

We can find the height of the image using $m = \frac{h_i}{h_o} = -\frac{d_i}{d_o}$

The magnification is $m = -\frac{d_i}{d_o} = -\frac{-0.091 \text{ m}}{1 \text{ m}} = 0.091$ times

so the image height is $h_i = mh_o$
$$= (0.091)(1.73 \text{ m}) = \textbf{0.16 m}$$

The positive sign means it's upright, as we expected.

Simple Optical Systems

When we put a couple of lenses together, or a lens and a mirror, we have a simple optical system. Some simple optical systems are microscopes and telescopes. The idea here is that the image of the first lens, even a *virtual* image, becomes the *object* for the second. The whole point of doing this is to get a final image that's magnified more than the image from just one lens.

We can make a simple optical system by putting together a converging and a diverging lens, like this:

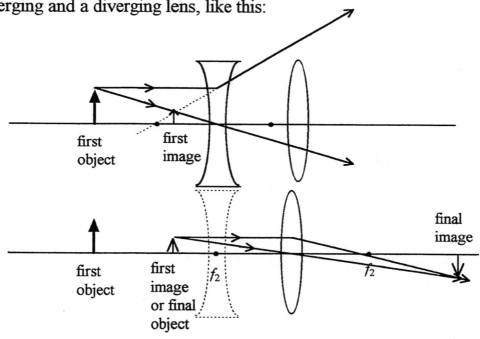

The object in front of the diverging lens is the **first object**, and the diverging lens creates the **first image** from this object. The first image becomes the *object* for the converging lens, and is called the **final object** (first image and final object are the same thing). The image produced by the converging lens is the **final image**. We can use the thin lens equation, and the magnification equation to analyze simple optical systems.

Example: *A diverging lens of focal length $f_1 = -3$ cm is put 4 cm to the left of a converging lens of focal length $f_2 = 4$ cm. If the first object is 6 cm to the left of the diverging lens, what does the first image look like? What does the final image look like?*

We'll find the first image, from the diverging lens.

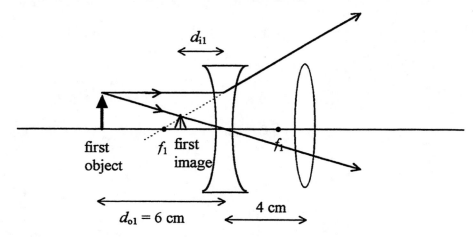

We see that the image is an upright, smaller, virtual image. We can find its location using the thin lens equation.

$$\frac{1}{f} = \frac{1}{d_o} + \frac{1}{d_i}$$

so

$$\frac{1}{d_i} = \frac{1}{f} - \frac{1}{d_o} = \frac{1}{-3 \text{ cm}} - \frac{1}{6 \text{ cm}} = -0.5 \text{ 1/cm}$$

$d_i = -2$ cm   Negative means a **virtual** image,

which is what we see in the ray diagram.

The magnification is $m = -\dfrac{d_i}{d_o} = -\dfrac{-2 \text{ cm}}{6 \text{ cm}} = 0.067$ times

The first image is upright, virtual, 2 cm to the left of the diverging lens, and magnified 0.067 times. This is the final object; the object for the converging lens.

We'll draw the ray diagram for the converging lens, with the first image as the object. The distance from the first image to the converging lens is equal to the first image distance plus the distance between the lenses:

$$d_{o2} = d_{o1} + 4 \text{ cm} = 2 \text{ cm} + 4 \text{ cm} = 6 \text{ cm}$$

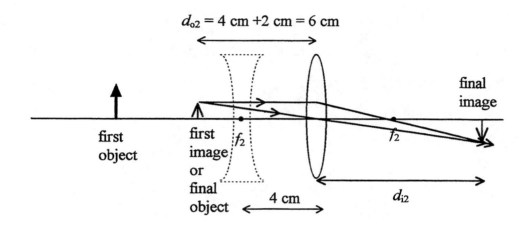

$$d_{o2} = 4 \text{ cm} + 2 \text{ cm} = 6 \text{ cm}$$

The final image is inverted, and real. The location of the final object is

$$\frac{1}{d_i} = \frac{1}{f} - \frac{1}{d_o} = \frac{1}{4 \text{ cm}} - \frac{1}{6 \text{ cm}} = 0.083 \text{ 1/cm}$$

$d_i = 12 \text{ cm}$ Positive means a **real** image, which is what we see in the ray diagram.

The magnification is $\quad m = -\dfrac{d_i}{d_o} = -\dfrac{12 \text{ cm}}{6 \text{ cm}} = -2 \text{ times}$

We can find the magnification of the *final image* relative to the *first object* by multiplying the two magnifications together:

final $m = 0.067$ times x -2 times = -0.134 times

The final image is inverted, real, 12 cm to the right of the converging lens, and magnified -0.134 times when compared to the first object.

The microscope: A microscope has two converging lenses, one called the **eyepiece** (the one closest to the eye), and the other is the **objective** (close to the first object). The light rays from the first object (the object of the objective lens) form a *real* and inverted first image. This first image becomes the final object (the object for the eyepiece), and the rays are again refracted, this time by the eyepiece. The light rays from the eyepiece converge to form a big final (virtual) image, like in the diagram below. The final image is inverted with respect to the first object, but upright with respect to the final object.

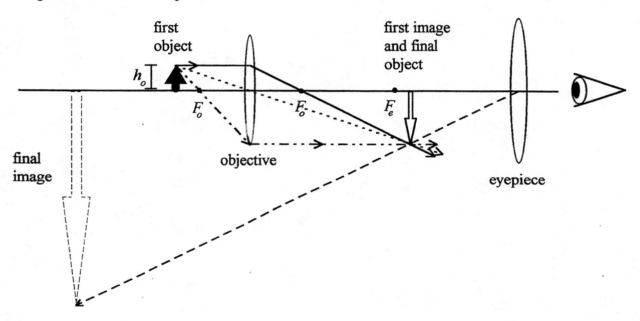

The lenses in a microscope are chosen to have small focal lengths, so that the magnification is larger.

The telescope: The telescope also has two converging lenses, also called the objective and the eyepiece. A telescope is different from a microscope because the first objects (stars and planets) it's designed to magnify are very far away, and we want the final image to be *smaller* than the first object.

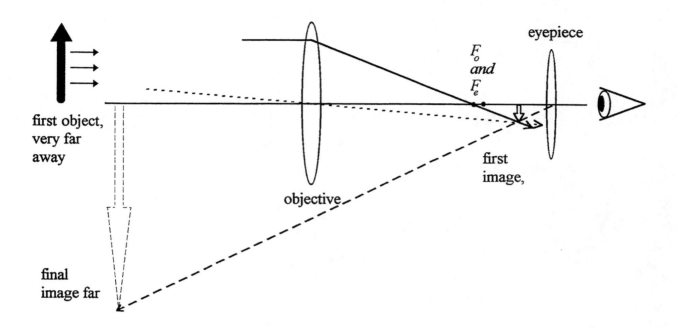

A telescope is made so that the first image is just inside the focal length of the eyepiece. The first image is smaller, inverted and real. The final image is big, but not *nearly* as big as the first object. The final image is also very far away from the telescope, inverted with respect to the first object, and virtual.

PHYSICS GRADE 11

Geometric Optics Practice Problems

1. A light ray hits the water of a fish tank at an angle of 30° to the surface (the index of refraction of water is 1.33). The tank has a glass bottom.
(a) What's the angle refracted ray light ray refracted by the water ?

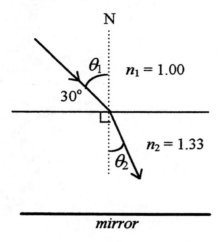

(b) What's the angle of reflection after the ray is reflected off the mirror ?

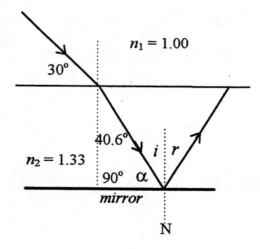

1. (c) When the light hits the surface of the water again, what will be the angle of refraction in the air ?

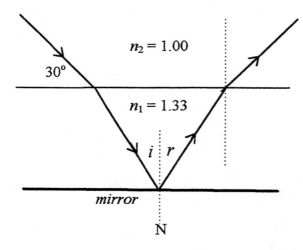

(d) If the depth of the tank is 0.55 m, how far to the right is the ray emerging from the water relative to the point where it went it ?

2. What is the index of refraction of a clear solid have to be if the critical angle of light is 52°, and the incident medium is air ?

3. Light hits a prism at an angle of incidence of 30°. If all the prism angles are 45°, and the speed of light in the prism is 2.04×10^8 m/s, what's the angle of the refracted light leaving the prism ?

4. Michelle wants to buy the smallest plane mirror that will let her see her full height. If she's 170 cm tall, and her eyes are 10 cm below the top of her head, what's the height of the mirror?

5. The focal length of a concave mirror is 5.0 cm.

(a) What is the radius of curvature ?

(b) What kind of image with you see if the object is placed:
        (i) 15 cm from the mirror.

        (ii) 8 cm from the mirror.

        (iii) 4 cm from the mirror.

(c) What kind of image will you see if the object is placed 8 cm in front of a convex mirror with focal length of 5.0 cm ?

6. A 2.0 cm high object is placed 4.0 cm in front of a concave mirror (f = 5.0 cm). Draw a ray diagram, describe the image, and find the location and height of the image.

7. A converging lens with f = 6.0 cm is used to magnify an object on the left side of the lens. The image is also on the left side, 10.0 cm away from the lens. (a) Draw a ray diagram (b) Describe the image (c) Find the location of the object and calculate the magnification.

8. A diverging lens has a focal point 8.0 cm away from the lens. An object is placed 10 cm from the lens. Where is the image and what does it look like?

9. Two converging lenses are used to make a microscope. The focal length of the objective is 1.1 cm, and the focal length for the eyepiece is 3.0 cm. They are 6.0 cm apart, and an object is placed 1.5 cm from the objective. Where's the final image and what's it's magnification?

10. For the lenses in question 9, what is the distance you would put between them apart to make a telescope? Why?

PHYSICS GRADE 11

Geometric Optics Practice Problem Solutions

1. A light ray hits the water of a fish tank at an angle of 30° to the surface (the index of refraction of water is 1.33). The tank has a glass bottom.
(a) What's the angle refracted ray light ray refracted by the water ?

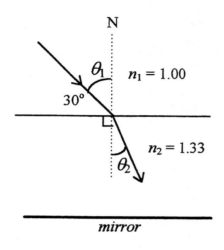

The angle of incidence is

$$90° - 30° = 60°,$$

so

$$\sin\theta_2 = \frac{n_1 \sin\theta_1}{n_2}$$

$$= \frac{1.00 \sin 60°}{1.33}$$

$$= 0.651$$

and so $\theta_2 = \mathbf{40.6°}$

(b) What's the angle of reflection after the ray is reflected off the mirror ?

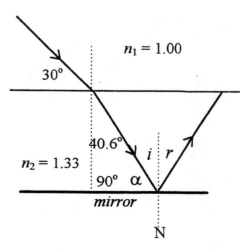

The angle of incidence on the mirror can be found using geometry:

We know that the angle in a triangle add up to 180°, so

$$\alpha = 180° - 40.6° - 90°$$

$$\alpha = 49.4°$$

and

$$\alpha + i = 90°,$$

and so $49.4° + i = 90°$, so $i = 40.6°$

Since the angle of incidence equals the angle of reflection,

$$r = \mathbf{40.6°}$$

1. (c) When the light hits the surface of the water again, what will be the angle of refraction in the air ?

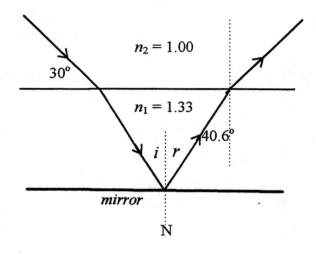

Using the same geometry as we used in (b), we find the angle of incidence on at the surface of the water is 40.6° again. Notice that n_1 and n_2 are reversed now, since the ray hits from the other side of the water.

so

$$\sin\theta_2 = \frac{n_1 \sin\theta_1}{n_2}$$

$$= \frac{1.33 \sin 40.6°}{1.00}$$

$$= 0.866$$

and so $\quad \theta_2 = 60°$

The light comes out at the same angle that it when into the water!

(d) If the depth of the tank is 0.55 m, how far to the right is the ray emerging from the water relative to the point where it went it ?

We can use trig to do find this. Use the right angle triangle that the ray reflected from the mirror makes with its normal line. The angle is 40.6°, and the adjacent side (the depth) is 0.55 m,

so

1/2 distance = (0.55 m) tan 40.6°
1/2 distance = 0.47 m

so **the distance between the incident and emerging light rays is 0.94 m**

2. *What is the index of refraction of a clear solid have to be if the critical angle of light is 52°, and the incident medium is air ?*

$$\sin\theta_c = \frac{n_2}{n_1}$$

so

$$n_1 = \frac{n_2}{\sin\theta_c} = \frac{1}{\sin 52°} = 1.27$$

$$n_1 = \mathbf{1.27}$$

3. *Light hits a prism at an angle of incidence of 30°. If all the prism angles are 45°, and the speed of light in the prism is 2.04×10^8 m/s, what's the angle of the refracted light leaving the prism ?*

First, we find the index of refraction of the prism.

$$n = c/v = (3.00\times10^8 \text{ m/s})/ (2.04\times10^8 \text{ m/s})$$

$$n = 1.47$$

We can then find the angle of the angle refracted in the prism:

$$\sin\theta_2 = \frac{n_1\sin\theta_1}{n_2} = \frac{1.00 \sin 30°}{1.47} = 0.340$$

and so $\qquad \theta_2 = \mathbf{20°}$

We use geometry to find the other angles, as shown in the diagram. We can find as we did in previous problems that the angle of

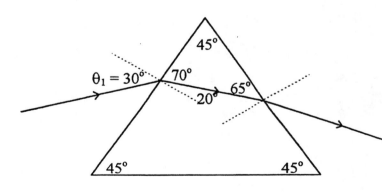

incidence for the ray exiting the prism is 25°. This means, using Snell's law,

$$\sin\theta_2 = \frac{n_1\sin\theta_1}{n_2} = \frac{1.47 \sin 25°}{1.00} = 0.621,$$

so $\theta_2 = \mathbf{38°}$

---

4. Michelle wants to buy the smallest plane mirror that will let her see her full height. If she's 170 cm tall, and her eyes are 10 cm below the top of her head, what's the height of the mirror?

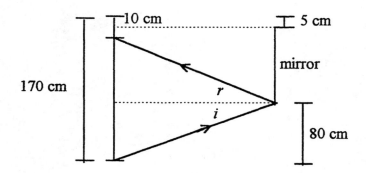

The shortest mirror will be placed such that a ray from her feet will hi the bottom of the mirror, and be reflected into her eyes. Since $<i = <r$, the point of reflection will be halfway between her feet and eyes,

$$\text{or} \quad \frac{\text{distance from feet to eyes}}{2} = \frac{170 \text{ cm} - 10 \text{ cm}}{2} = 80 \text{ cm}.$$

The mirror's bottom edge has to be 80 cm from the floor.

A ray from the top of her head will hit the top edge of the mirror, and be reflected into her eyes. This point of reflection will be halfway between the top of her head and eyes,

$$\text{or} \quad \frac{\text{distance from top of head to eyes}}{2} = \frac{10 \text{ cm}}{2} = 5.0 \text{ cm from}$$

the top of her head.

The height of the mirror is then (looking at the diagram)

$$170 \text{ cm} - 5 \text{ cm} - 80 \text{ cm} = 85 \text{ cm}$$

The mirror height is 85 cm, or half of her height.

5. *The focal length of a concave mirror is 5.0 cm.*

(a) What is the radius of curvature ?

radius of curvature: $R = 2f = 2(5.0 \text{ cm}) = \textbf{10 cm}$

(b) What kind of image with you see if the object is placed:
(i) 15 cm from the mirror.

real, smaller, and inverted

(ii) 8 cm from the mirror.

real, bigger, and inverted

(iii) 4 cm from the mirror.

virtual, bigger, and upright

(c) What kind of image will you see if the object is placed 8 cm in front of a convex mirror with focal length of 5.0 cm ?

The image produced by a convex mirror is always **virtual**,

upright, and **smaller** than the object.

6. *A 2.0 cm high object is placed 4.0 cm in front of a concave mirror (f = 5.0 cm). Draw a ray diagram, describe the image, and find the location and height of the image.*

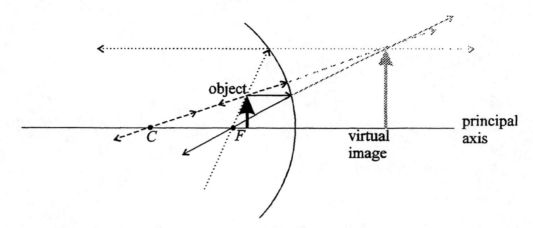

The image is virtual, upright, and bigger than the object.

We can find the d_i using the mirror equation.

$$\frac{1}{d_o} + \frac{1}{d_i} = \frac{1}{f}$$

f and d_o are positive, so

$$\frac{1}{d_i} = \frac{1}{f} - \frac{1}{d_o} = \frac{1}{5.0 \text{ cm}} - \frac{1}{4.0 \text{ cm}} = -0.05 \text{ 1/cm}$$

so $d_i =$ **20 cm**   (a negative d_i, so the image is

virtual and behind the mirror)

The magnification is $m = -\dfrac{d_i}{d_o} = -\dfrac{-20 \text{ cm}}{4.0 \text{ cm}} = 5.0 \text{ times}$

$$m = \frac{h_i}{h_o}$$

$$h_i = m \, h_o = 5 \,(2\text{cm}) = \textbf{10 cm}$$

7. *A converging lens with f = 6.0 cm is used to magnify an object on the left side of the lens. The image is also on the left side, 10.0 cm away from the lens. (a) Draw a ray diagram (b) Describe the image (c) Find the location of the object and calculate the magnification.*

(a)

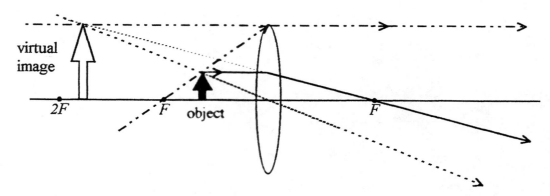

(b) The image is virtual, larger and upright

(c) Use

$$\frac{1}{d_o} = \frac{1}{f} - \frac{1}{d_i}$$

$$= \frac{1}{6.0 \text{ cm}} - \frac{1}{-10.0 \text{ cm}}$$

$$= 0.267 \text{ 1/cm}$$

$$d_o = \textbf{3.75 cm}$$

$$m = -\frac{d_i}{d_o} = -\frac{-10 \text{ cm}}{3.75 \text{ cm}} = \textbf{2.7 times}$$

8. *A diverging lens has a focal point 8.0 cm away from the lens. An object is placed 10 cm from the lens. Where is the image and what does it look like?*

$$\frac{1}{d_i} = \frac{1}{f} - \frac{1}{d_o}$$

$$\frac{1}{d_i} = \frac{1}{-8.0 \text{ cm}} - \frac{1}{10 \text{ cm}}$$

$$= -0.225$$

$$d_i = \textbf{-4.4}.$$

The image is **virtual, smaller and upright**.

9. *Two converging lenses are used to make a microscope. The focal length of the objective is 1.1 cm, and the focal length for the eyepiece is 3.0 cm. They are 6.0 cm apart, and an object is placed 1.5 cm from the objective. Where's the final image and what's it's magnification?*

We find the location of the first image using the objective

$$\frac{1}{d_i} = \frac{1}{f} - \frac{1}{d_o} = \frac{1}{1.1 \text{ cm}} - \frac{1}{1.5 \text{ cm}}$$

$d_i = 4.2$ cm from the objective.

$$m = -\frac{d_i}{d_o} = -\frac{4.2 \text{ cm}}{1.5 \text{ cm}} = -2.8 \text{ times}$$

The d_o for the eyepiece is 6.0 - 4.2 cm = 1.8 cm

$$\frac{1}{d_i} = \frac{1}{f} - \frac{1}{d_o} = \frac{1}{3.0 \text{ cm}} - \frac{1}{1.8 \text{ cm}} = -0.22 \text{ 1/cm}$$

$d_i = \textbf{-4.5 cm the final image is 4.5 cm to the right of the eyepiece.}$

$$m = -\frac{d_i}{d_o} = -\frac{-4.5 \text{ cm}}{1.8 \text{ cm}} = 2.5 \text{ times}$$

$$m_{total} = (-2.8) \times (2.5) = \textbf{-7 times}$$

10. *For the lenses in question 9, what is the distance you would put between them apart to make a telescope? Why?*

Put them 4.1 cm apart, so that their focal points coincide.

Light and the Wave Model

We've spent a good chunk of this book describing what happens to waves and light rays at boundaries. The whole point of this is to try to figure out the nature of light. We assumed in the last section on geometric optics that light travels only in straight lines. For the most part, this is an OK assumption, but what happens when we have very sharp edges ? What happens if we shine light through a slit, like we did for waves ? Does it still look like light only goes in straight lines ? If it doesn't, we're going to have to look further that geometric optics to explain the behaviour of light. In this, the last section of this book, we're going to find that light acts an awful lot like a wave.

Snell's Law and Light Waves

Remember Snell's law of refraction ?

$$n_1 \sin\theta_1 = n_2 \sin\theta_2$$

$$\text{or } \frac{\sin\theta_1}{\sin\theta_2} = \frac{n_2}{n_1}$$

Remember that we defined the index of refraction, n as $n = c/v$, the speed of light in a vacuum divided by the speed of the light in the medium. We can substitute this into the Snell's law equation, and find

$$\frac{c}{v_1}\sin\theta_1 = \frac{c}{v_2}\sin\theta_2$$

$$\frac{\sin\theta_1}{v_1} = \frac{\sin\theta_2}{v_2}$$

$$\text{or } \frac{\sin\theta_1}{\sin\theta_2} = \frac{v_1}{v_2}$$

Now, if we follow the thought that light can behave as a wave, we can use the wave equation $v = \lambda f$ in the version of Snell's law we just found. This

gives us $\quad \dfrac{\sin\theta_1}{\sin\theta_2} = \dfrac{\lambda_1 f}{\lambda_2 f} = \dfrac{\lambda_1}{\lambda_2}$,

since the wavelength is different in the two mediums, but the frequency isn't. This gives us the complete version of **Snell's law:**

$$\boxed{\frac{\sin\theta_1}{\sin\theta_2} = \frac{n_2}{n_1} = \frac{v_1}{v_2} = \frac{\lambda_1}{\lambda_2}}$$

If is relation is true, then we should see that different wavelengths of light are refracted different amounts. This is *exactly* what we see in a prism, where the white light is split into its component colours. Here we have some evidence that light can behave as a wave.

Reflection, Refraction and the Particle Theory of Light

We know that light travels through outer space. We also know there is no air; outer space is *really* empty. If light was a wave (like a sound wave), there would be no medium through which it could propagate. This is one reason why many people think light is a particle, or at least has particle-like properties.

There's evidence to support this theory, like reflection and refraction. Anyone who's played much pool knows that a pool ball bounces off the side of the table at the same angle it hit.

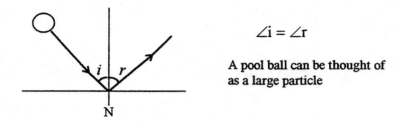

$\angle i = \angle r$

A pool ball can be thought of as a large particle

This is just like the law of reflection of light we talked about in geometric optics.

We can do a simple experiment to see if particles refract at boundaries. A simple way of doing this is rolling a ball on a flat table, toward an incline, and see what happens if it hits the incline at an angle. The incline changes the velocity of the ball, so we can think of it as a change in the medium.

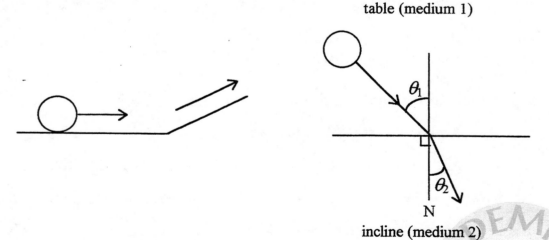

table (medium 1)

incline (medium 2)

We see that the ball is refracted. Doing some more experimentation will show us that the refraction obeys Snell's law

$$\frac{\sin\theta_1}{\sin\theta_2} = \frac{v_1}{v_2}.$$

Particles can be reflected and refracted in the same we saw that light is reflected and refracted. This suggests that light behaves like a particle, and that geometric optics can explain the behaviour of light. Unfortunately, it's not as simple as this, as we'll see in the next few pages.

Reflection, Refraction and the Wave Model of Light

We talked about reflection and refraction of mechanical waves in an earlier section of this guide. You may remember that we found that waves reflect when they hit some surfaces. I described how waves hitting the side of a swimming pool reflect at the same angle at which they hit; the angle of incidence equals the angle of reflection. This is exactly what we saw in geometric optics with light hitting mirrors, and when we reflected pool balls (particles). It looks like either a wave of a particle model will explain the reflection of light.

What about refraction ? We refracted waves in a swimming pool too. We found that when waves moved to a different depth of water (a different medium), the wavelength of the waves changed, and the angle of wave propagation changed. In fact, if we did some more experiments and took some measurements, we find that wave refraction obeys our new version of Snell's law,

$$\frac{\sin\theta_1}{\sin\theta_2} = \frac{\lambda_1}{\lambda_2}.$$

It also looks like *we can explain refraction with either light waves or light particles*.

Young's Double Slit Experiment

When we learned about waves, we found out that the principle of linear superposition resulted in wave interference (remember interference is the canceling and amplification of wave crests and troughs when two waves are in the same place a the same time). In 1801, Thomas Young did an experiment that changed the way we thought of light. He found that light could produce *interference patterns*. This *proved* that light was a wave, or at least acted like a wave sometimes. It also was a method that allowed him to find the exact wavelength of the light.

Young set up the experiment like the one diagrammed below. There's one thin slit, S_o, cut in a screen. This is placed in front of two thin slits cut in another screen, S_1 and S_2. Light going through S_o will be from the same spot on the light source. This is important, because the light that hits S_1 and S_2 *has* to be in phase (when a crest hits S_1, a crest has to hit S_2). If the light isn't in phase, the experiment won't work. We say S_1 and S_2 are **coherent** sources of light. A screen is placed a distance l from the double slits. It's on the screen that the interference pattern is seen.

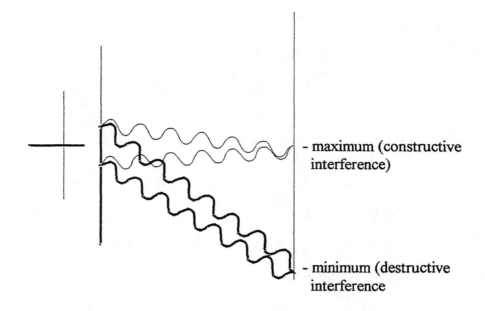

Young's Experiment

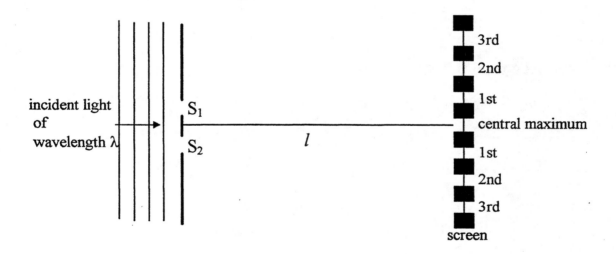

The interference pattern is a series of light and dark bands, or **fringes**. The bright fringes are cause by constructive interference. A light wave coming from S_1 interferes constructively with a light wave coming from S_2, which means they meet crest-to-crest and trough-to trough at the screen. The dark bands are caused by destructive interference; the waves meet crest-to-trough at the screen.

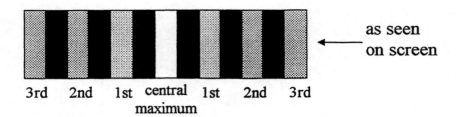

3rd   2nd   1st   central   1st   2nd   3rd
                     maximum

The brightest fringe is in the centre, the **central maximum**. The bright fringes get less and less bright (and the dark fringes get bigger) as you move further away from the central maximum. The other bright fringes are numbered, as shown in the picture above. .

We can find the wavelength (λ) of the incident light using

$$\lambda = \frac{dx}{nl}, \quad \text{where } n = 1, 2, 3,...$$

d is the distance between the slits (measured from their centres), l is the distance from the slits to the screen, and x is the distance between the central maximum and the other bright fringe (like in the figure below). n is a whole number, determined by the fringe number you're using, counted from the central maximum.

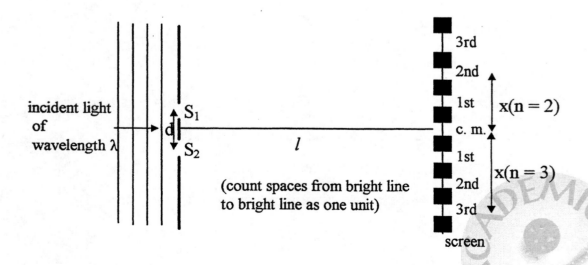

Example: *If Young used two slits, 1.20 x 10^{-4} m apart, the screen was 1.2 m from the slits, and the distance between the central maximum and the second bright fringe was 1 cm, what was the wavelength of the light ?*

We can use $\lambda = \dfrac{dx}{n\mathit{l}}$ to find the wavelength of the light.

Remember that 1 cm = 0.01 m

$$\lambda = \dfrac{dx}{n\mathit{l}} = \dfrac{(1.20 \times 10^{-4} \text{ m})(0.01 \text{ m})}{2(1.2 \text{ m})}$$

$$\lambda = \mathbf{5.0 \times 10^{-7} \, m, \text{ or } 500 \, nm}.$$

This is blue-greenish light.

Diffraction of Light

You might remember from the sections before that diffraction is the bending of waves around obstacles. It is an interference effect. If light travels only in straight lines, we wouldn't ever see diffraction from a light source. If light diffracts, then there's more evidence that light shows wave-like characteristics. Diffraction of light has been seen by shining light through a single thin slit, an through small holes. We know there's diffraction happening because the screen in front of the slit of hole has a fuzzy pattern on it, instead of one bright spot.

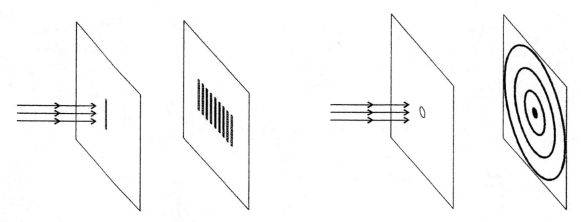

Another way we have observed the diffraction of light is by shinning light through a **diffraction grating**. A diffraction grating is a plate with up to *thousands* of thin slits. It works the same way as Young's double slit experiment worked, light coming through one slit interferes with the light coming through the other slits. There are just a lot more slits. We get a diffraction pattern that looks like a bunch of Young's double slit experiment patterns put end to end. The diagram below shows a series of maxima, sometimes called **principal fringes**.

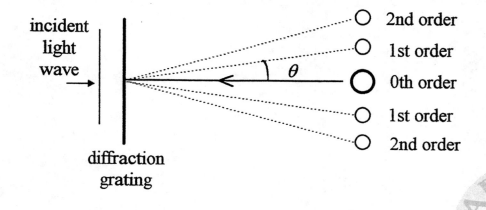

Each of the 0th to 2nd order maxima in the diagram have smaller fringes on either side, but they are very hard to see, especially as the number of lines in the grating increases. The screen might look something like this:

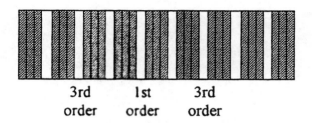

3rd   1st   3rd
order   order   order

The white fringes are the principal maxima, and the gray fringes are secondary maxima. A diffraction grating gives a much sharper image than a double slit.

We can find the wavelength of the light used with:

$$\lambda = \frac{d \sin \theta}{n}$$

where   n is 1 for 1st order fringe, or n is 2 for 2nd order fringe, etc

d is the distance between the lines in the grating

and θ is the angle measured from the central line to the line connecting the image from centre of the diffraction grating (like in the first diagram on this page).

Example: *Light of wavelength 410 nm hits a diffraction grating. If the angle from the 0th order principal maximum to the 2nd order principal maximum is 40°, what is the number of lines per cm ?*

We can use $\lambda = \dfrac{d \sin\theta}{n}$, to find the distance between the lines.

so $\qquad\qquad d = \dfrac{\lambda n}{\sin\theta}$

Now n = 2 , since the angle is measured to the second order principal fringe, and remember that 410 nm = 410 x 10^{-9} m.

so $\qquad\qquad d = \dfrac{(410 \times 10^{-9}\,\text{m})(2)}{\sin 40°}$

$$d = 2.55 \times 10^{-6}\,\text{m}$$

This is the distance between the lines in meters. We want the *number* of lines per cm. We find the number of lines per meter by inverting d:

number of lines per m $\quad = 1/d = 1/(2.55 \times 10^{-6}\,\text{m})$

$$= 3.92 \times 10^{5}\ \text{lines/m}$$

We want to convert to centimeters, so

$$= 3.92 \times 10^{5}\ \text{lines/m} \times 10^{-2}\ \text{m/cm}$$

$$= 3.92 \times 10^{3}\ \text{lines/cm}$$

There are 3920 lines/cm on the diffraction grating.

Both Young's double slit experiment and diffraction tells us the same thing, light acts like a wave at least part of the time. These behaviours can't be explained by geometric optics, which is based on the particle model of light. *Diffraction and interference give us evidence that light has wave properties.* But wait! There's even more evidence!

Polarization

If light is a wave transverse wave (that's the one where the particle vibrations are perpendicular to the direction of propagation), we should be able to **polarize** light. **Polarization** happens when all the up and down vibrations occur in only one plane.

If we make waves in a rope, we can make the wave parallel to the floor, perpendicular to the floor, or somewhere in between. Normally, light waves will have particle vibrations in all these directions. When we polarize the waves, we cut out all but one of these directions (maybe we only keep the vibrations perpendicular to the floor. We can do this by passing the light through a polarizing filter, like this:

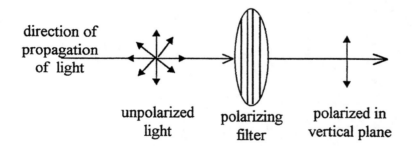

Only the light with vertical particle vibrations will pass through the filter. If we put another filter like the one above, but rotated it 90°, all the light would be blocked; the component parallel to the floor would be blocked by the first filter, and the component perpendicular tot the floor would be blocked by the second filter.

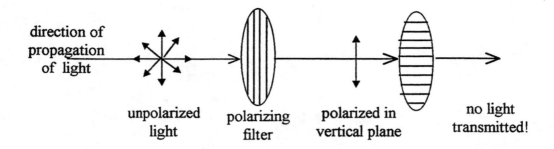

Polarizers are very useful things, and are used in sunglasses, among other things. The polarizers in the lenses of sunglasses work by cutting out the horizontally oriented light. This cuts down on the amount of light that hits your eyes.

If light were a beam of particles, we wouldn't expect that any of them would stopped by the polarizer. If light were a compression wave, all the light would get through, since the vibration is in the same direction of travel. *The phenomenon of light polarization gives us evidence that light is a transverse wave.*

We can't use geometric optics to explain interference, diffraction and polarization. If light were just straight beams of particles, we wouldn't expect to see these behaviours. The only explanation we have for these behaviours is the one presented here; *that light behaves like a transverse wave.*

PHYSICS GRADE 11

Light and the Wave Model Practice Problems

1. Why does light interference phenomena prove that light was wave properties ?

2. In a double slit experiment, the distance from the screen to the double slit is 1.3 m. The wavelength of the light used is 400 nm, and the second maximum is 0.020 cm from the central maximum.
(a) What's the slit separation ?

(b) How would the fringe pattern change if the light waves hitting both slits were shifted by a half wavelength ?

What if the light were shifted a half wavelength through one slit ?

3. We can use a diffraction grating to see the colours in light. If a light is made up of violet and red light waves, find the angle between the central maximum and the first order maximum for each colour ($\lambda_v = 410$ nm, $\lambda_r = 660$ nm). The diffraction grating has 5.0×10^3 lines/cm.

PHYSICS GRADE 11

Light and the Wave Model Practice Problem Solutions

1. Why does light interference phenomena prove that light was wave properties ?

Interference patterns happen when wave troughs and crests coincide, and they superimpose to cancel and reinforce each other. This can't be explained if light were just a particle. Since we see interference patterns with light, it has to act like a wave when it passes through the slit, or the grating.

2. In a double slit experiment, the distance from the screen to the double slit is 1.3 m. The wavelength of the light used is 400 nm, and the second maximum is 0.020 cm from the central maximum.
(a) What's the slit separation ?

$$400 \text{ nm} = 400 \times 10^{-9} \text{ m} = 4.00 \times 10^{-7} \text{ m}$$

and
$$0.020 \text{ cm} = 0.00020 \text{ m}$$

We can rearrange $\lambda = \dfrac{dx}{n l}$ to find the wavelength of the light.

$$d = \frac{\lambda n l}{x} = \frac{(4.00 \times 10^{-7} \text{ m})(2)(1.3 \text{ m})}{(0.00020 \text{ m})}$$
$$d = 5.2 \times 10^{-3} \text{ m}$$

(b) How would the fringe pattern change if the light waves hitting both slits were shifted by a half wavelength ?

No change, since the light is still coherent.

What if the light were shifted a half wavelength through one slit ?

The dark and light fringes would switch positions (there would be a central minimum instead of a central maximum).

---

3. *We can use a diffraction grating to see the colours in light. If a light is made up of violet and red light waves, find the angle between the central maximum and the first order maximum for each colour* $(\lambda_v = 410$ nm, $\lambda_r = 660$ nm$)$. *The diffraction grating has 5.0×10^3 lines/cm.*

We can use $\;d = \dfrac{\lambda n}{\sin\theta}\;$ to find the angles.

We first find the slit separation:

$$d = 1/(5.0 \times 10^3) \text{ cm} = 2.0 \times 10^{-4} \text{ cm} = 2.0 \times 10^{-6} \text{ m}$$

and remember that

$$410 \text{ nm} = 410 \times 10^{-9} \text{ m} = 4.10 \times 10^{-7} \text{ m}$$
$$660 \text{ nm} = 660 \times 10^{-9} \text{ m} = 6.60 \times 10^{-7} \text{ m}$$

now

$$\sin\theta = \frac{n\lambda}{d}$$

so

violet light: $\;\theta_v = \sin^{-1}\left(\dfrac{n\lambda_v}{d}\right) = \sin^{-1}\left(\dfrac{1(4.10 \times 10^{-7} \text{ m})}{2.0 \times 10^{-6} \text{ m}}\right) = \mathbf{11.8°}$

and

red light: $\;\;\;\theta_r = \sin^{-1}\left(\dfrac{n\lambda_r}{d}\right) = \sin^{-1}\left(\dfrac{1(6.60 \times 10^{-7} \text{ m})}{2.0 \times 10^{-6} \text{ m}}\right) = \mathbf{19.3°}$

ORDER FORM
Call 1-800-403-4751
www.aestudyguides.com

STUDY GUIDES	BASED ON CANADIAN CURRICULUM			
	ISBN 13	QTY	PRICE	EXTENDED
Math Grade 7	9781552020548		34.95	
Math Grade 8	9781552020531		34.95	
Math Grade 9	9781552020562		34.95	
Math Grade 10 **PURE**	9781552021101		37.95	
Math Grade 11 **PURE**	9781552021118		37.95	
Math Grade 12 **PURE**	9781552021125		37.95	
Math 13/Math 11 - Intro	9781552020067		34.95	
Math 23 Grade 11	9781552020470		34.95	
Math 33 Grade 12	9781552020081		34.95	
Calculus Grade 12 / University	9781552020609		54.95	
Language Arts Grade 7	9781552020746		34.95	
Language Arts Grade 8	9781552020753		34.95	
Language Arts Grade 9	9781552020760		34.95	
Grammar Basics All Grades	9781552020777		34.95	
English Grade 10	9781552020784		34.95	
English Grade 11	9781552020791		34.95	
English Grade 12	9781552020807		34.95	
Science Grade 7	9781552021002		28.95	
Science Grade 8	9781552021019		28.95	
Science Grade 9	9781552021026		28.95	
Science Grade 10	9781552021033		31.95	
Social Studies/History Grade 7	9781552020210		28.95	
Social Studies/History Grade 8	9781552020227		28.95	
Social Studies/History Grade 9	9781552020234		28.95	
Social Studies/History Grade 10	9781552020494		34.95	
Social Studies/History Grade 11	9781552020258		34.95	
Social Studies/History Grade 12	9781552020265		34.95	
Physics Grade 11	9781552020272		37.95	
Physics Grade 12	9781552020289		37.95	
Biology Grade 11	9781552020296		37.95	
Biology Grade 12	9781552020302		37.95	
Chemistry Grade 11	9781552020319		37.95	
Chemistry Grade 12	9781552020395		37.95	
Shipping - Retail Orders	Subtotal			
1 Study Guide: $8.50	Shipping			
Each Additional: $3.00	GST 5%			
	Total:			

STUDY BUDDY'S
CANADIAN CURRICULUM

	ISBN	QTY	PRICE	EXTENDED
SB Math	9781552020920		42.95	
SB Read'g	9781552020937		31.95	
SB Spel.	9781552020944		35.95	
SB Writing	9781552020951		37.95	
SB Science	9781552020968		32.95	
SB Soc. St.	9781552020975		35.95	
			Subtotal	
Shipping - Retail Orders				
1 Study Guide: $8.50				
Each Additional: $3.00				
			Shipping	
			GST 5%	
			TOTAL:	

PURCHASER INFORMATION

Name: _____

Address: _____

City: _____ Prov: _____

Postal Code: _____ Phone: _____

Payment Method: (Please check one)

❏ Cheque ❏ Visa ❏ MasterCard

Name on Card:

_____

Card #: _____

Signature: _____

SCHOOL PURCHASE ORDERS #'S ACCEPTED

Telephone or prepaid orders may be sent to:

876 Verdier Avenue
Brentwood Bay, BC V8M 1B9
Phone 1-800-403-4751
Fax 1-800-661-6087

We Appreciate *Your* Business.

Go Beyond Your Limits With **THE ACADEMIC EDGE LTD.**